LIFE NATURE LIBRARY

THE
FOREST

TIME
LIFE
BOOKS
®

LIFE WORLD LIBRARY

LIFE NATURE LIBRARY

TIME READING PROGRAM

THE LIFE HISTORY OF THE UNITED STATES

LIFE SCIENCE LIBRARY

INTERNATIONAL BOOK SOCIETY

GREAT AGES OF MAN

TIME-LIFE LIBRARY OF ART

TIME-LIFE LIBRARY OF AMERICA

FOODS OF THE WORLD

THIS FABULOUS CENTURY

LIFE NATURE LIBRARY

THE FOREST

by Peter Farb
and the Editors of
TIME-LIFE BOOKS

TIME-LIFE BOOKS   NEW YORK

About the Author

Peter Farb is a student of forests and the plant and wildlife relationships that make them up. A graduate of Vanderbilt University, he is a Fellow of the American Association for the Advancement of Science, former Secretary of the New York Entomological Society, and a member of the Ecological Society, the Soil Conservation Society, the American Institute of Biological Sciences and other scientific organizations. As a contributor to many magazincs, Farb has written widely on natural history. He is the author of several books, among them *Living Earth* and *Face of North America: the Natural History of a Continent*. For six years Farb studied the interrelationship of plants and animals in an outdoor laboratory in upstate New York.

On the Cover

Mature California redwoods tower over young saplings. The redwood, or *Sequoia sempervirens*, world's tallest evergreen tree, has been known to attain a height of 364 feet and a girth of 63 feet. The most aged redwood thus far found dates back more than 2,000 years.

Contents

TIME-LIFE BOOKS

EDITOR
Maitland A. Edey
EXECUTIVE EDITOR
Jerry Korn
TEXT DIRECTOR   ART DIRECTOR
Martin Mann   Sheldon Cotler
CHIEF OF RESEARCH
Beatrice T. Dobie
PICTURE EDITOR
Robert G. Mason
Assistant Text Directors:
Harold C. Field, Ogden Tanner
Assistant Art Director: Arnold C. Holeywell
Assistant Chief of Research: Martha T. Goolrick

•

PUBLISHER
Rhett Austell
Associate Publisher: Walter C. Rohrer
Assistant Publisher: Carter Smith
General Manager: Joseph C. Hazen Jr.
Business Manager: John D. McSweeney
Production Manager: Louis Bronzo

•

Sales Director: Joan D. Manley
Promotion Director: Beatrice K. Tolleris
Managing Director, International: John A. Millington

LIFE NATURE LIBRARY

EDITOR: Maitland A. Edey
Assistant to the Editor: George McCue
Designer: Paul Jensen
Chief Researcher: Martha T. Goolrick
Researchers: Barbara Ballantine, Judith Bloom, Doris Bry,
Joan Chasin, Susan Freudenheim, Paula Norworth,
Roxanna Sayre, Michael Schwartz, Paul W. Schwartz

EDITORIAL PRODUCTION
Color Director: Robert L. Young
Copy Staff: Rosalind Stubenberg, Suzanne Seixas,
Florence Keith
Picture Department: Dolores A. Littles, Joan T. Lynch, Sue Bond
Traffic: Arthur A. Goldberger
Art Assistants: James D. Smith, Mark A. Binn

The text for the chapters of this book was written by Peter Farb, the picture essays were written by John Brick. The following individuals and departments of Time Inc. were helpful in producing the book: LIFE staff photographers Eliot Elisofon and Dmitri Kessel; Editorial Production, Robert W. Boyd Jr.; Editorial Reference, Peter Draz; Picture Collection, Doris O'Neil; Photographic Laboratory, George Karas; TIME-LIFE News Service, Murray J. Gart.

Introduction

MAN's relationship to the forest has undergone many striking and complex changes during the few millennia since the advent of civilization. The human form probably was cradled by the forest—particularly such attributes as its upright position and the opposable thumb. The vegetable products and game of the forest fed and clothed early man. However, as his agricultural skills developed, the forest became a liability. Forests were eliminated from much of Europe and the British Isles even before the discovery of America. European settlers chopped, sawed and burned their way across half of this newly discovered continent in a few centuries. Some trees were used in construction, some to make corduroy roads, others for cooking and heating, but most were rolled into huge piles and burned. Today this process is continuing in southern Asia and the Philippines as well as in many other parts of the world.

When farmland has replaced a large portion of the forest, the population will suddenly discover that it is no longer possible to go into a nearby wood lot and cut enough trees to supply its requirements for lumber and fuel. Suddenly the need for conservation, for increased productivity and proper utilization of the remaining forest lands becomes apparent. This awakening occurred several centuries ago in Europe, although the advent of scientific forestry is much more recent. In America the necessity for protecting forests and growing trees for future needs has been recognized for less than a hundred years. Today we know the forest as an important source of building materials and a vast reservoir from which modern technology can derive a virtually unlimited number of valuable products such as paper, plastics, turpentine and alcohol.

But the forest is much more than a warehouse for man's material needs. Its protective covering is renowned as a conservator of soil and water and as a moderator of local climate. The visitor-pressure on our national, state and local parks and forests is unprecedented and has surpassed even the most liberal estimates made a decade ago.

Peter Farb has written an absorbing book. Through a careful selection of superb photographs and their combination with an illuminating text he and the editors of TIME-LIFE BOOKS have achieved a goal for which many other authors have strived. The concept of the forest as a community of living things whose lives are inextricably intertwined with one another and bound to their physical environment presents an intellectual challenge that will enrich anyone's future contact with the forest. It is my personal hope that every reader will adopt this dynamic philosophy of the forest and let it guide his future decisions as a citizen.

JACK MCCORMICK
Chairman
Department of Ecology and Land Management
The Academy of Natural Sciences of Philadelphia

1

The
Forest
Year

To the casual eye, one patch of woodland looks very much like another. This is far from true; the arrangement of trees in a landscape is precise and follows laws of bewildering complexity. Every forest is the outcome of an intricate chain of events in climate, earth history, soil development and many other factors—which have shaped the landscape and determined the kinds and numbers of trees growing there. Although several dozen species of trees may be "common" here and there throughout a given temperate region, their abundance within a particular forest varies widely. Some trees associate with others in one place, with still others in a different place. Certain species are found only in swamps, others primarily atop mountains where their roots grip rocks or maintain a precarious hold in the thin layer of soil; some are partial to the shaded north sides of hills, but there are others that thrive only on sun-flooded slopes.

Level all the trees of a forest with chain saws and within a few hundred years a new forest will have sprung up, almost indistinguishable from the one that was destroyed. Where a hemlock may have grown once, a hemlock will grow again—and it will be accompanied by the community of other plants and animals unique to a hemlock forest. The replacement of hemlock by hemlock does not happen immediately, though. The forest first must pass through a fascinating sequence of stages—weeds, scrub, sun-enduring trees and so forth—each of which makes the land hospitable for the next wave of growth. Finally, a stage is reached beyond which there is little change, barring some calamity of insect plague or disease epidemic, fire, earth shift or man's interference. The "climax forest," as it is called, perpetuates itself endlessly with only minor alterations, a bastion against encroachment by other kinds of trees that may flood it with their seeds year after year in vain.

Trees are only the most imposing members of the forest community of life. Associated with them—using them as support, growing in their shade, dependent on the high humidity that the canopy of leaves maintains—may be more than a thousand kinds of shrubs, vines, herbs, ferns, mosses and toadstools in even a small woodland. In addition, the forest swarms with insects, mammals, birds, reptiles and amphibians. The numbers of all these members of the community are in delicate balance and tied to each other by invisible threads of food, living conditions and mutual cooperation. This multitude of life does not merely live in the forest—it *is* the forest as much as the trees themselves. So intricate is the tapestry of forest life that should a single vital thread somehow be broken, the entire pattern might unravel and ultimately the forest itself be destroyed.

To North Americans, the procession of seasons that explodes through the forest seems the most natural thing in the world. The familiar woods of the eastern United States and southern Canada lie in the great world-wide Temperate Zone—a place wracked by extremes of climate that belie its very name. In summer it may be hotter than in the shimmering tropics; in winter it suffers the bite of northern winds and icy droughts, for the water supply is locked up tight in the snow and the frost in the soil. Under the challenges of the seasons, the everyday woods of the Temperate Zone undergo remarkable rhythms of growth and decay, death and rebirth.

The winter forest stands stripped of its leafy finery, the soil frozen hard, sounds muffled by the white blanket of snow—yet its apparent barrenness is an illusion. The multitude of living things of the summer forest is still present—invisible under the snowdrifts, hidden in the bark of trees, in tree holes and stumps and rocky dens. There is an abundance of microscopic life in the Lilliputian world of the microorganisms that dwell near the surface on individual grains of soil. Even those forms that have temporarily deserted the forest, the migrating birds, carry with them the remembrance of the very woods in which they were fledged and will attempt to return there when winter has passed.

Those pillars of the forest, the trees, have, through long ages of evolution, developed a method of adjusting to the drought of winter. Most of them (except for the evergreens) simply shut down. They do this by shearing off their broad leaves, which are prodigal of water, in order to preserve the supplies of moisture contained in the cells of root, trunk and branches before the ground froze. In this way they remain as dormant as drought-stricken cacti until spring. Plants that have developed this life-saving mechanism are known as "deciduous," from a Latin word meaning "to fall off." It is a

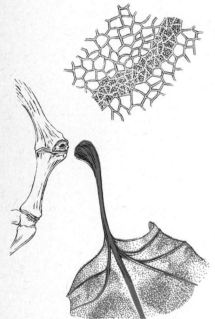

LEAF FALL occurs after a delicate abscission layer of cells (*see detail*) forms, causing the stem of the leaf to break off. A corky tissue remains, covering the exposed scar on the twig.

mighty fall: as many as 10 million leaves may flutter down onto a single acre of woodland.

The tree does not shut down its immense system of waterworks each fall until it has made advance preparations for the greenery of another year. Growing at the base of nearly every stalk, where last year's leaves were connected to the twigs, is the promise of another spring—the winter buds, perhaps several million of them on a large tree. Each is an exquisite miniature, a master plan of all the elements that will make for renewed growth. There is a hoard of sugars for food, there is a cluster of cells possessing the ability to divide rapidly, there are embryo leaves—all enveloped in an armor of scales that defend the tender tissues against winter drought (not against cold, as is commonly supposed). The practiced eye of the woodswalker can identify most trees by the winter buds alone, since each species possesses its own design. Dogwood-flower buds are shaped somewhat like toadstools, the leaf buds like a bird's bill. Beech trees wear buds encased in thick scales of a striking bronze hue. Shagbark hickory buds are covered by scales with long graceful points. Inside the scales the new leaves are folded carefully like parachutes, and they unfurl in spring without a blemish. Some embryo leaves are folded like fans, others rolled like cigars.

FOREST animals have developed methods no less remarkable whereby they survive the harshness of winter and long periods of food shortage. Some birds migrate thousands of miles to areas where lessened food is not a problem. For the miracle of migration there is an equivalent marvel for the stay-at-homes—hibernation. The depth of winter sleep in forest animals varies from short periods of torpor, with little reduction in body temperature, to the true hibernation of some animals that seem balanced on a razor's edge between life and death. So complete is the winter sleep that these animals can be handled, some even thrust in water without awakening them. For the hibernator, as winter approaches there is a mysterious change in the internal mechanisms that have maintained an even body temperature during the year. Each minute during its active period, the heart of the woodchuck, for example, beats roughly 80 times. But when it rolls up in its underground burrow in the autumn and passes into slumber, its pulse slows to only four or five beats a minute and its body temperature may drop to a few degrees above the freezing point. Its body metabolism is still operating, like the dimly burning pilot light on a gas stove, but at a rate just sufficient to sustain life.

A chipmunk's winter sleep is somewhat less sound; it awakens occasionally in its burrow under the soft drifts, uncurls and feeds on the supply of seeds it accumulated in the autumn. Snakes, being cold-blooded, must remain in warm dens until the temperature rises in spring. Many insects suspend life, surviving winter as dormant eggs or in cocoons, and sometimes even as torpid adults; a few remain in the caterpillar stage, like the woolly bear, and spend the winter protected under logs, emerging during thaws to crawl on the forest floor.

Winter is the season the Indians called "the long sleep," but tracks in the snow reveal that not all animals are hibernating or have fled the forest. Those links in far-reaching food chains, the preyers and the preyed upon, manage to eke out an existence despite the winter. Deer, which neither hibernate nor store a supply of food, forage during the night, nibbling the tender twigs and buds not covered by snow. The deer's only seasonal adaptation is the growth of a winter coat of hollow hairs that traps a blanket of warm air against its body. The fox continues its pursuit of rabbits even in the coldest weather. The woodpecker's food supply is scarcely reduced by winter; it continues to drill under the bark of trees to find insects hidden there. And in the woodland pond, the beaver lives off its cache of tender bark and twigs which it stored in the autumn in the deepest water near its lodge.

As the snow begins to melt in March and the sun warms the ground, the pace of forest life quickens. The mourning cloak butterfly occasionally rouses itself from its torpor and takes wing through the open glades. As they grow at the margin of the woodland stream, skunk cabbages generate temperatures several degrees higher than their surroundings; sometimes they even poke their hoods of foul-smelling leaves through the lingering snows. Unseen changes take place inside the trees as buds prepare to fling out their green banners. The sun floods the blanket of litter that covers the soil like a hothouse roof, raising the soil temperature. Farmers festoon the sugar maples with sap buckets and bluebirds return to small tree holes in the forest. By the time sugar-making is completed and the bluebird has chosen the site for its nest, it is spring.

The spring flood of life flows upward like a fountain—rising from the thawing soil, tinging the forest floor with a mist of green, and then bursting in an emerald spray as millions of leaves in the upper tiers of the forest break out of their buds. Earthworms begin tunneling upward in a vertical migration, and the appearance of their little mounds of digested soil on the damp surface is no less a harbinger of spring than the returning bluebirds. The burrows of chipmunks open; toads emerge unharmed after being frozen into their mud cellars; and at the pond a one-inch frog, the spring peeper, sends out a far-carrying mating call that sounds like a bird's song. There is incredible activity in a rich forest soil: as many as 1,350 creatures visible to the naked eye or with a magnifying glass may be found in an area a foot square and an inch deep, and that does not include the billions of microscopic organisms in every handful of earth. As they feed, these tenants of the soil break down the litter of leaves and dead branches into elements that can be assimilated by the growing plants; were it not for them, the forest might in a few years be choked by its own wastes.

The blazing leaves of autumn that dropped to the floor six months before are found to be a dull, monotonous brown when the snow melts. But the faded litter is soon stirred by the flowering plants—hepaticas, trilliums, violets, spring beauties and others that sprinkle daubs of color through the woods. This burst of color is no accident. Small plants must do their blooming in the spring—while the sunlight can still reach them, before the canopy of tree leaves obliterates the sky.

The awakening of life within the speck of a seed is the result of complex changes. A growth hormone becomes active and enzymes effectively regulate and direct the development of the plant; fat and starch stored within the seed are converted into sugarlike chemicals; the store of proteins is broken up into some 20 compounds which are rushed to the growing points of stem and root where other enzymes arrange them into building materials. In spite of all this activity, the woodland seeds often seem strangely reluctant to germinate. Many are equipped with mechanisms that deliberately delay sprouting

—perhaps a waterproof coat that requires a long period, sometimes years, for moisture to soften and then penetrate it; perhaps a requirement that the seed be chilled for a long time (occasionally *two* cycles of chill and thaw). Delayed germination has great survival value for plants that exist in a region of sudden weather changes. Were it not for these mechanisms, a seed might sprout in the warm days of Indian summer or during a February thaw, only to be killed by the return of winter.

The timetable of blooms on the woodland floor is unfailing every year and marvelously precise—skunk cabbages in March, hepaticas in April, birds-foot violets in May. Why May? Why do not violets bloom in autumn the way asters do? The answer has long eluded botanists, but it is now known that the constantly changing relationship of daylight to darkness, as the seasons progress, is the trigger that sets off the blossoming of flowers. This response of plants to the steadily shortening nights of spring, or to the steadily lengthening nights of fall, is known as photoperiodism. Almost every plant has a trigger in it which awaits the proper photoperiodic signal for its cells to stop growing stems and leaves and start growing flowers and seed. A hormone that no one has ever seen, but which has nevertheless been named florigen, moves through the plant and directs the multiplying cells toward building flower structures. Photoperiodism governs much of the sequence of forest life. The buds which burst forth with the rising temperature of spring, usually on schedule according to species, were formed during the previous summer and fall in response to the lengthening nights, and remain dormant throughout the winter. Photoperiodism also plays an important part in root formation and the growth of stems and leaves. It affects birds as well as plants. The migrating song sparrows, mourning doves, warblers and other woodland species are prisoners of photoperiodism and definitely not the free agents of the wood they were once believed to be. Their return northward is triggered by the lengthening days of spring which heighten activity of their reproductive glands. When the days get long enough, the birds *must* go north to breed.

Birds are the most conspicuous forest animals and in the spring they make it a singing woods. Their torrent of song is not a hymn to the joy of an awakened year, as poets keep saying, but is caused by belligerency and possessiveness during the mating season. As soon as the male birds return to the forest they stake out territories. These vary in size, depending on many factors: season, food supply, size of the bird and so forth. Each bird seems to, know how big a territory it needs to feed a family of fledglings. Once chosen, a territory is vigorously defended against intrusions by other birds of the same species. These holdings are advertised by constant song from favorite singing posts along their borders, a proclamation of the extent of the territory and the determination to defend it. The variety of songs is impressive: the cardinal may have 28 different ones, and 884 song variations have been recognized in song sparrows. Nonsingers have other methods for declaring the boundaries of their territories. Woodpeckers hammer their beaks on dead limbs; the male ruffed grouse drums on a log or stump by rapidly fanning air against it with its wings.

An acre of forest may hold two or three pairs of nesting birds, each of whose young may require its own weight of food every day. But so varied is the life of the forest that each pair offers little competition to other species nesting nearby but inhabiting different "niches." Four different kinds of woodpeckers—pileated, hairy, downy and red-bellied—may nest in the same woods. They all dig insects out of the bark of trees but each species is a specialist in different parts of trees and there is no conflict. At the same time and in the same forest, flycatchers take insects on the wing and thus offer little competition to the woodpeckers, while the ground territory is worked over for food by cardinals, ovenbirds and towhees, and wood warblers hunt in the higher stories. In the three-dimensional world of the spring forest, each form of life finds its own place with the same rigidity that restricts human beings to their own rooms in an apartment house.

As spring progresses and trees clothe themselves with leaves, a riot of every subtle shade of green spreads over the forest. Leaves are great food producers. They take carbon dioxide from the air, water from the soil, light from the sun and use them—by a process known as photosynthesis—to manufacture sugars and starches. The amount of water taken up by the roots is prodigious. A tree in full leaf may lift a ton of water a day from the soil and carry it through an intricate system of pipelines to every leaf. About half of the food produced by the tree is retained, going into new growth of trunk, branches and far-reaching root system; the other half goes into operating the food-making machinery, into replenishing the expendable leaves and into repairing damaged parts of the tree.

The oaks, last to lose their leaves in the autumn, are the last to gain them in the spring. When they finally unfold their greenery, closing over the canopy and shutting out the sky, summer has come. Early summer is the muted season of contentment, serenity and incredible abundance; the closed canopy makes for deep shadows, high humidity and the stifling warmth of an incubator. So thick are the leaves that they can be heard brushing against one another in the wind—the whining of the pines, the crackling of elms, the faint tremolo of the aspens. The sounds of the woods have always intrigued visitors nearly as much as the sights; 2,000 years ago the Roman poet Virgil wrote of an oak in southern Europe that "gave tongue to the wind." Each kind of leaf seems to have its own method of flapping in the wind. This is determined by its shape and the way it is attached to its twig, even the flexibility of the twig itself. Aspen leaves flutter in a breeze, as if a thousand green butterflies were on the twigs, opening and closing their wings. The stems of aspens are flat and act like sails that catch the faintest breath of air. The stems of oak leaves act like springs and their motion is to flap up and down. Willow leaves are attached to whiplike branches and they sweep back and forth like pendulums.

The visitor to a summer woods cannot fail to notice how hushed the animal life is. The springtime chorus at the pond is silent, and the stream that rushed and gurgled only a few months before is reduced to a brown trickle. The bark of the fox is no longer heard and few birds sing, except the indefatigable ovenbird. At this time many animals enter a state similar to the torpor of winter. The chipmunk eats almost nothing during the summer hot spells, and as a result of its decreased metabolism keeps itself comparatively cool. The woodland toads dig shallow burrows and press their bodies against the cool moist earth under the blanket of leaves. The reptiles enter a period of inactivity and venture out of their dens only in wet weather or after sundown. Night is now the busy time. As the sun sets, the opossum slowly travels to the ground for its evening's foraging, its movement from limb to limb aided by its long bare tail which serves as a fifth leg, one of the many physical adaptations to a forest existence found among woodland dwellers. The porcupine spends much of the night stuffing itself with bark and foliage. From the surrounding fields birds fly into the forest, seeking safe resting places. There is also a nighttime flow of traffic in the opposite direction as raccoons, foxes, skunks and deer all search for food beyond the margins of the woods.

Summer is insect time, and foliage suffers. The leaves that were unfurled in all their perfection a few months ago are now drooping tatters, like banners after a storm. Scarcely a square inch of plant tissue escapes the attention of one or more species, insects which chew at the edges of leaves, rob sap from trunk and leaves, suck at roots, even mine passageways between the minute cells of the leaves themselves. But such is the relationship of all life in the forest that a caterpillar which eats leaves one summer may produce a butterfly that pollinates the flowers of the same plant the following spring.

Insects thrive in warm weather and their moisture demands are low. They reach a height of activity in the dry hot days of July and August and until the killing scythe of frost sweeps through the forest, the treetops sound with their orchestra. The male snowy tree cricket fiddles: it has a series of ridges on one wingcover, like the strings of a violin, and a thickened vein on the other wingcover, which may be compared to the bow. Drawing the vein back and forth over the ridges produces a call that somewhat resembles the sound made by a creaking door. Only the males call—and only they have the delicate hearing equipment for receiving these sounds; the females are soundless and deaf. The call is believed to be a declaration of territory, uttered for much the same reason that birds sing in the spring. The katydid, camouflaged to resemble a leaf, plays a fiddle of a different design on its wings; during the course of a summer a single katydid may draw its bow between 30 and 50 million times. During the day, the forest sounds belong to the cicadas. They add their monotonous drumming to the summertime orchestra, and 2,000 years ago Virgil remarked that "they burst the very shrubs with their noise."

Leaves that survive insect attacks are withered by dry winds and become stained by the spreading films of fungi. A perfect leaf can scarcely be found by the end of summer. Now when the breeze blows through the trees, a few leaves begin to flutter to the ground and sunlight again flashes through the canopy above. The forest appears increasingly threadbare and so does much of the life that inhabits it. Birds go into retirement while they exchange their bright breeding plumage for the drabber one of winter. Mammals are shedding before growing their heavy coats; the squirrel's tail shrinks to a few scant bristles of hair, making it almost useless as a stabilizer. Until a new bushy tail grows, the squirrel will not be so adventurous; no longer will it fling itself from tree to tree across the forest canyons.

Two hundred years ago the governor of the Massachusetts Bay Colony wrote home to England about the American deciduous woods: "If I should persuade the Painter to attempt the giving a real and strict Portrait of these Woods in Autumn, he must mix in upon his Canvass all the Colours of the Rainbow, in order to copy the various and varied dyes which the Leaves at the Fall assume." Autumn in the New England woods must have astounded the early settlers. The color that flies from the trees and the carpet

ADAPTATION TO COLD, illustrated by a saw-whet owl, is typical of many birds. Smooth feathers (*above*) can be fluffed (*below*) to trap air, thus conserving the bird's body heat.

of gold, red and vermilion on the forest floor can be seen almost nowhere else in the world. Temperate deciduous forests exist on other continents, but they lack the colorful diversity of species of the American paintpot. Here the red maple becomes as bright as a pyre that seems to light up the whole woods. Puffs of red burst from sugar maples, sumacs send out crimson flares and the poplars bedeck themselves with colors of old gold.

Contrary to belief, it is not frost that paints the autumn woods; rather, each blaze of color heralds a subtle change in the internal chemistry of the leaf. The cool, dry days of autumn trigger a complicated sequence in trees, a sequence that involves shutting down their huge waterworks. In summer each leaf begins to prepare for its own death by forming at the base of its stem a layer of thin cells, sometimes visible to the naked eye as a light-colored band on the leafstalk or a furrow running around its base. Directly beneath this layer, another will form cells to heal the scar which will be made when the leaf falls off. As these two layers grow, they clog the pipelines to the leaf. The green chlorophyll is no longer renewed; it breaks down quickly and disappears, revealing the riot of other colors—yellow, gold and orange—that were in the leaf all summer long, but masked by the chlorophyll. In addition to this, another group of pigments that in most cases were not in the leaf at all during the summer is produced. These pigments create the dramatic reds, scarlets and purples.

While some of the leaves are still brightening with color, those of other species are already fluttering to the forest floor. The cells at the base of each leaf stem disintegrate, gradually detaching the leaf until it is held to the twig only by the connecting veins that supplied it with water and nutrients during the summer. A gentle breeze or even a few raindrops are enough to break these fragile strands and leaves rain down by the millions, piling up in colorful drifts. The pigments remain in the leaves for a short time, but soon they too break down, all except the brown tannins, and the forest floor is carpeted with a monotonous drabness.

ANIMALS that remain active throughout the winter have special adaptations. Many accumulate thick layers of fat and luxuriant winter coats. The ruffed grouse, which will remain in the woods all winter, grows long scales on its toes; these act as snowshoes to support the bird as it walks in the snow. Little animals of the forest floor prepare for cold-weather food shortages by gathering surprisingly large hoards of seeds and nuts and stocking them in granaries. A single squirrel may hide away 20 or more bushels of food divided into many small caches, although it may not find and eat a tenth of that reserve before spring.

For most insects, the approach of winter brings death. Occasionally a katydid or cicada sings into Indian summer, but it is a lonely, plaintive sound that reminds the woodswalker of the departed fruitfulness. Despite the slowing down of the pace of life, there is no true end of the forest year, for each season nurtures the next. There is promise of rebirth in the winter buds, the eggs of a multitude of insects, dormant roots, seeds, animals suspended in torpor. This continuity of life and its extraordinary variety and richness of forms have never ceased to cause wonder in those who study the familiar woods. The great scientist Louis Agassiz, who found infinite drama in the everyday things around him, once said: "I spent the summer traveling. I got halfway across my backyard."

Cycle of the Seasons

BLOODROOT, NAMED FOR THE ORANGE SAP OF ITS STEM AND ROOTS, SPREADS SPRING BLOSSOMS IN A NORTH CAROLINA FOREST

An endless sequence of splendors unfolds annually in the wood-lands of eastern North America. Extremes of climate produce seasonal changes that rarely can be matched anywhere else in the world. Winter has an arctic fierceness, spring creates an intoxicating distillation of fragrance and rebirth, summer a trop-ical somnolence, and autumn is literally a brilliant explosion.

A DAY-OLD WOOD DUCK peers from its nest in a hollow tree. Though the nests may be 40 feet high, baby ducks jump down. They are so fluffy, they do it without injury.

THE MOCCASIN FLOWER, or pink lady's-slipper, is one of about 140 North American orchids. Nectar in its prominent "lip" draws insects that take its pollen to other plants.

WHITE CARPETS OF FRINGED PHACELIA (*opposite*) bloom in the Great Smoky Mountains National Park, where about 1,300 native species of flowering plants have been recorded.

Spring

Among the first signs of spring in the eastern woodland is the appearance of small, delicate flowers like spring beauty. These are only a few inches tall and must get started quickly or they will be barred from the sun by other, taller plants unfolding above them. Snowdrops actually bloom in the snow: they have a rich cell fluid which resists freezing and they can draw on the food stored in bulbs beneath the surface.

All forest life is geared to a complex and delicate clockwork. Robins arrive in time to greet the worms tunneling up from deep in the ground. Swarms of flying insects mist the air, but if a cold snap comes they lie stunned in the weeds and the flocks of early swallows which feed on them starve. Meanwhile, in orderly succession, the trees spread a green awning: first the lowest shrubs, then the dogwoods, finally the tall oaks and hickories. By mid-June the woods lie deep in shade.

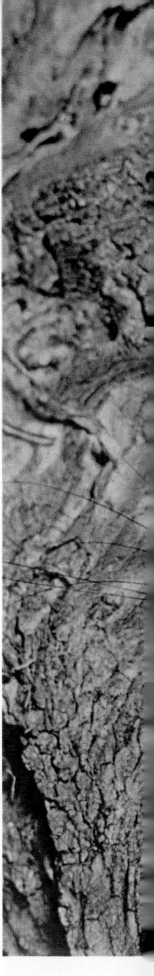

HIDDEN NEST shelters young cottontail rabbits. Born furless and blind, they leave the nest at two weeks, live apart from their mother at two months and can breed at six months.

GAPING MOUTHS of newborn song sparrows (*left*) wait for a meal. Blind and helpless for 10 days, they are fed 11 times an hour and their weight increases tenfold during the same period.

WIDE EYES of the three baby flying squirrels (*right*), as well as their long sensitive whiskers, are adaptations well suited to their nocturnal lives. They do not fly, but glide between trees.

CLEAR POOLS AND SHADED BANKS lie along the quiet summer course of a stream in a North Carolina mountain park. Scenes like this were once common in the forest belt that extended from Canada to northern Florida, but are now limited to preserves like the Great Smoky Mountains National Park, located in North Carolina and Tennessee.

This park, covering 507,159 acres, is about one fourth virgin forest, the largest such tract in the eastern United States. Within it are found 130 species of native trees.

OPOSSUM FAMILY climbs a red maple tree under a summer moon. A baby possum is the size of a bee at birth and lives eight weeks inside its mother's marsupial pouch.

Summer

Summer is insect time, seen in the clouds of Mayflies hatching from woodland brooks, heard in the humming of the cicada that dies within a week, after a nymphal life below ground of perhaps 17 years. Some scattered flowers, tolerant of shade, bloom beneath the dense canopy. Orange touch-me-nots, favored by humming-birds, ripen seed pods that explode if touched. Tall yellow foxgloves attach themselves parasitically to tree roots for food. Forest creatures react to inhibiting heat: gray squirrels flatten themselves on moist earth and turtles dig into cool mud, while fish seek deep pools. Bees, however, work at top speed in the hot dry days.

A WHITE-TAILED DEER gazes from a thick cover. As long as it is standing still it holds its tail down, but when it begins to run, the tail goes up like a white flag to warn other deer.

A COMMON BOX TURTLE, tugging at an earthworm, is named for its ability to box itself tightly inside its shell. It reaches full growth at 20 years and often lives to be 80.

A WHITE-FOOTED MOUSE (*right*) eats jack-in-the-pulpit berries. Mainly nocturnal, it has several litters of young each year, sometimes using vacated bird or squirrel nests.

WOODLAND MUSHROOMS sprout among scattered leaves at the base of a lichen-covered tree in a Maine forest. These three, which favor a hardwood habitat, are among the hundreds of varieties that are commonly found in the woods during the "mushroom months" of August and September.

The clustered yellow cylindrical stalks at center are coral mushrooms, or *Clavaria fusiformis*. The bluish growths to their left are violet *Cortinarius*. The encircling groups of red-orange fungi are vermilion mushrooms, or *Hygrophorus miniatus*. Mushrooms, like all fungi, have no chlorophyll

themselves and must get their food directly or indirectly from other plants. They do this in three ways. Some, called obligate parasites, feed only on living plants. Others are facultative parasites, feeding on green plants until they kill them, then living on the dead plant tissue. But most are saprophytes, nourished by decaying remains of dead plants. They are therefore an immensely important link in the chain of growth and decay on the forest floor. Mushrooms have no seeds; they reproduce principally by spores, sometimes producing them at the rate of 40,000,000 an hour.

WILD TURKEY, ALERT TO DANGER, STANDS IN A FOREST GLADE

Autumn

During the short, fat harvest days of fall, there is a tremendous outburst of activity on the part of most wildlife. Trees scatter food everywhere on the forest floor—hickory nuts, acorns, beech-nuts, butternuts—and it is prodigiously eaten and stored by many birds and mammals. Rich forage grows in bright colors at low levels—the orange fruit of mountain ash, red witch-hobble berries, plump white snowberries. Beavers pile up more food than they can use in underwater caches near their lodges, favoring poplar bark if they can get it. The tireless raccoon stuffs itself at night to store fat for its winter sleep. Its wide range of foods includes fruit and nuts, frogs and crayfish. This is the time of big migrations for little birds, for thrushes, for warblers and king-lets which may travel from Canada to Brazil. They work their way through the woods, al-ways southward, eating as they go. Ice follows them, filming the edges of forest ponds. When the last flock is gone, autumn will be gone too.

28

THE GRAY FOX is the only tree-climbing fox. It hunts small animals and big insects, and eats abundant fall fruits. Its full coat is deceptive: adults weigh only seven to 11 pounds.

YOUNG COPPERHEAD, dangerous but not aggressive, has a yellow-tipped tail which it wiggles to lure its prey. It may share its winter den with other kinds of snakes.

BLAZING MAPLE LEAVES (*left*) in autumn help create a singular seasonal spectacle in the temperate forest of the Northern Hemisphere almost unknown below the equator.

GETTING READY FOR WINTER, some common animals are shown in an imaginary scene which extends from September at left to the first snows of December at right. In the air monarch butterflies, a brown creeper (*right center*) and geese (*rear*) escape the cold by migrating south. But downy woodpeckers (*red topknot*) and ptarmigans (*far right*) are hardy and stay north all winter, the latter diving into snowbanks to keep warm and escape enemies. On the ground, a chipmunk conceals its hole with leaves, preparatory to hibernating. The skunk and fox do not hibernate

RUDOLF FREUND

but forage actively in late fall to fatten themselves, while the she-bear sleeps in her cave, awaiting the birth of her cubs. Below ground, both chipmunk and blacksnakes have curled into balls. Though the snakes' eyes stay open, they are too drowsy to notice the nearby rabbit. Turtles and

frogs settle deep in the mud, barely breathing all winter. The perch, caught in a frozen pool, will survive if there is a thaw before its body is frozen solid. For the brook trout (*far right*), early winter is mating time and the female, fat with eggs, looks for a place to deposit them.

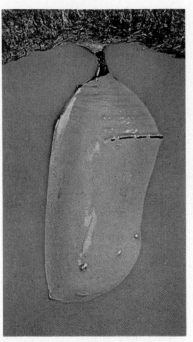

THE MONARCH'S METAMORPHOSIS, FROM CATERPILLAR TO BUTTERFLY, LASTS 12 DAYS AFTER THE CHRYSALIS IS COMPLETED

READY TO FLY, a monarch rests after pumping blood into its wings to stretch them. This must be done quickly, or they will stay shriveled and the monarch will never fly.

The Flight of "The Wanderer"

One of the most remarkable of migrations is that taken each fall by the North American monarch butterfly. Often called "the wanderer," it is tough and powerful as butterflies go, and is capable of long flights at a speed of 20 miles an hour or more. The monarch produces as many as four generations a year, each one of which ventures a little farther north. It is the last of these which migrates before the oncoming of winter. From as far north as Canada, swarms of butterflies begin gathering from their homes in the fields, clinging to trees and bushes by the thousands. Then, on just the right breeze, they rise in a red cloud and head south. Not all get there. But enough do to ensure the survival of the species until the following spring.

Monarchs have extraordinary powers of flight. They have been observed within 200 miles of the coast of England, although not native to Europe. They are also now found in Asia and Australia, perhaps having been carried there by the wind.

MIGRATING MONARCHS settle for the night on an oak at the forest's edge (*opposite*). These "butterfly trees" are used every year, although each adult makes the journey only once.

IN STILLNESS AFTER A WINTER STORM, SNOW ACCENTS THE BARE LIMBS OF FOREST TREES. EVERY SNOWFLAKE IN ITS PRISTINE

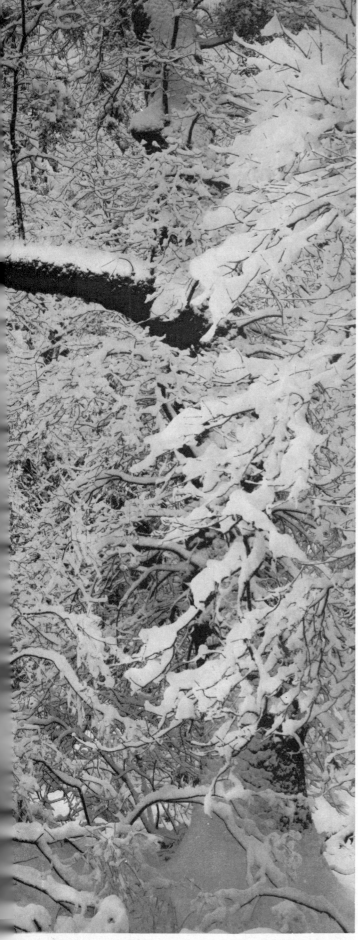

FORM IS HEXAGONAL, YET NO TWO ARE EVER EXACTLY ALIKE

TRAPPED MEADOW LARK tries to break through the crust that froze over its night roost in the snow. Some birds, like ruffed grouse, often dive headfirst into snow to sleep.

Winter

Snow is a protector of suspended life in winter woodlands, insulating all living things beneath it by trapping air in each intricate snowflake to slow the transfer of heat or cold. Snow shields dormant plants and animal hibernators from ground frosts and lashing winds, thus assuring spring abundance for all life that lies asleep. Snowbanks form water reserves for other seasons as the soil absorbs them gradually and deeply during thaws. The forest itself is a shelter; even when the trees are bare, storm winds in wooded lands are cut to 25 per cent of their force in adjacent open country. In spite of these moderating factors, the rigors of winter make movement and hunting food very difficult for the animals that move abroad.

STARVED TO DEATH, a deer sprawls in the snow. In a Wisconsin study, wardens found one frozen deer to every 12.3 acres; about half the deer had died of starvation.

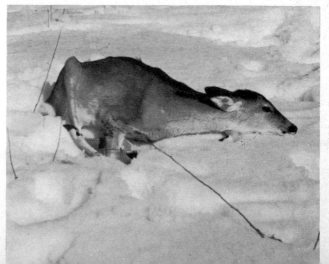

THE GRACEFUL SYMMETRY of a sugar maple, rising to the winter sky, is mainly due to the growth of its branches in pairs on opposite sides of the trunk. Its gray bark, deeply ridged as it ages, protects it from desiccating winter winds. Maples endure extreme cold when they are dormant, but are endangered by sudden sharp frosts in fall and spring.

GNARLED LIMBS of a white oak spread haphazardly in abrupt angles and curves. Each species of tree has its own characteristic skeleton, depending in part on the angle at which its twigs grow and also on whether it has a single trunk, like a pine, or whether the trunk branches into several heavy limbs. Both maple and oak fall in the latter category.

37

STUMP FOSSILS are relics of Lepidodendron trees killed by floods in Scotland 300 million years ago. Mud filled their decaying cavities and turned to rock to form the stump casts.

2

Ancient Landscapes

THE story of the evolution of forests may be read in nearly any deciduous woodland. Each is a living textbook of plant life, a pageant of vegetation that can be witnessed in a mere few dozen yards—for many of the plants of long ago have their representatives in the flora of today. In the shallow water of a forest pond are primitive plants that existed more than two billion years ago, before there was any life on land. These are the single-celled algae which form a green scum on the water. Along the edges of the pond, leading an amphibious existence, are liverworts, strange plants whose ancestors originated much more recently, perhaps 300 million years ago. A liverwort is a humble plant but it is well worth respectful consideration. Its ancestors surmounted immense obstacles in making the transition to a land existence. All living things must have water; in fact, every living cell of an organism must have it. That is no problem for a plant living *in* the water. But for the ancestors of the complex multicelled liverwort, attempting to rise into the dry air, braving wind and sun which were sure to deplete the water in the cells, this called for something entirely new—a plumbing system which would reach all the plant's cells and continually replace the water that was lost. More than that, certain cells had to become specialists in certain jobs—some absorbing water, others circulating it. Another problem for the liverwort was developing enough supports to hold it up in the air. A water plant simply floats, but a land plant needs specialized tissue to build a rigid skeleton. The liverwort solved both these problems after a fashion. But, despite its advance, its grasp on the land is a tentative one. It lacks roots and an efficient plumbing system. Thus it is severely limited in the height it can attain in the struggle for light in the forest.

Also along the margin of the pond are dense thickets of horsetails, whose forerunners first appeared about 320 million years ago. Horsetails are straight slender plants with jointed stems that somewhat resemble bamboo; although still wedded to a water existence, they possess rigid skeletons that lift their crowns of scalelike leaves straight into the air. In damp spots a little way from the pond are club mosses, which creep along the soil and look like pine trees in miniature. They display a further step along the road toward adapting to a land existence since they possess stems, leaves and a few weak roots.

IN other moist places throughout the woods are lacy ferns. Hundreds of millions of years ago their ancestors flourished in a variety of forms—as small plants and shrubs, or as tremendous trees that grew 60 feet high. Even now, although in temperate zones we know them best as delicate plants, they are found in the tropics as tree ferns with heights comparable to those of their tallest forebears. These ancient ferns were structurally very advanced for their time. They evolved true roots to probe for water and nutrients, sturdy systems of pipelines to carry water to the topmost cells in their leaves and rigid skeletons that could lift the leaves high into the sunshine. And yet they were still vulnerable to dry conditions. To reproduce they needed water.

Away from the pond now, and scattered throughout the deciduous woods, are found examples of another great development—evergreen conifers such as pines, hemlocks and spruces, whose ancestors were among the earliest seed plants. Seeds revolutionized the green mantle of the earth— for each possessed an entire plant embryo, packaged with a dowry of food from the parent plant, a speck of life that could spread and populate the earth. Instead of depending on a sperm that must thrash through water, a seed is the result of fertilization by a pollen grain, some varieties of which can float hundreds of miles through the air without drying out. Furthermore, the seed often remains on the parent tree, protected and nurtured while the embryo inside develops.

Freed from direct dependence on the water for reproduction, ancestors of pines spread over much of the earth, covering the plains and mountains, venturing into entirely new habitats. The ancient conifers and cycads seemed close to dominating all of the land when plants underwent still another improvement which led to the shrubs, vines, broad-leaved trees and hosts of wild flowers which make up most of the "modern" deciduous forest of today. This brings the journey through plant history up to the present, for the flowering plants are the latest fashion in vegetation. They

GREEN ALGA, or pond scum, is related to the earliest of all plant life. Each of its cells contains spiral ribbons known as chloroplasts, which carry on the organism's photosynthesis.

THE LIVERWORT may have descended from the green algae. Today it is still found growing flat along the ground, having no true roots, stems or leaves like the more advanced plants.

have two principal advantages over pines. Their seeds are better protected, developing enclosed in shells. And they have evolved flowers and fruits, precise devices for transferring pollen and dispersing seeds with the aid of insects, birds and mammals.

All these members of the forest community tell a continuing story of progress from one-celled algae to complex forest giants, from unspecialized plants to a modern profusion of flowers and leaf shapes, a journey from water to dry land. The journey requires only a few dozen yards as seen in a woodland, but it represents hundreds of millions of years of trial and error, blind alleys and dead ends in evolution. Many new avenues of development were taken by plants and then abandoned; structures were added, subtracted and added again; whole plant families vanished, leaving only records as fossils in rocks. The lords of the forest in one age became the underbrush of another. All this took place over periods of time so great that they stagger man's everyday time sense. Visualize the history of life on the planet as being compressed into a 24-hour day, with the first microscopic organisms originating at midnight and evolving and expanding as the day advances. It is not until about six p.m.—three fourths of the day already gone by—that life in the oceans becomes abundant. By eight p.m. plants invade the land, by nine p.m. the great coal-age forests flourish. Modern flowering plants do not develop until the late hour of 10:30 p.m. The recorded history of modern man does not begin until a quarter of a second before midnight.

Paleobotanists, those scientists who specialize in the study of ancient vegetation, are quite certain that plant life originated in the sea. The misty beginnings were probably about two billion years ago, with single-celled algae gradually developing into complex multicelled plants, and the oceans and swamps swarming with an increasingly varied animal life. Approximately 420 million years ago the first plant pioneers ventured out of the swamps and began an existence on the desolate land, a world of naked rocks unsoftened by a green mantle. No one knows definitely which plants successfully made the first hesitant steps to land, but they were undoubtedly borderline forms, developed from water weeds in the coastal swamps and still living a half-water, half-land existence. These plants were probably so insignificant they would merit scarcely a glance today and they were certainly not numerous; they lacked true roots and leaves and could not survive without being in continuous contact with moisture. Nevertheless, their foothold on land was secure; it was a staggering event for the history of the earth.

THAT the invasion of land was a success was seen by mid-Devonian times, roughly 375 million years ago, when a great surge of vegetation swept the earth. A landscape of this period would be a vaguely familiar world to us, perhaps resembling a scene in the swampy Florida Everglades. But many things would be missing from this dawn forest. The colors would be monotonous—the living vegetation a uniform green, the dead and decaying plants brown. No flowers would brighten the landscape. It would be a nearly soundless world, lacking the cries of birds and mammals, the hum of insects. In fact, animal life on land was still a rarity—only mites and several forerunners of insects and spiders had crawled ashore, the vanguard of a host that would soon populate the earth.

HORSETAILS are small replicas of ancestors that grew 40 feet high. They have two kinds of stems: one topped by a cluster of spore cases; the other a stem with whorled branches.

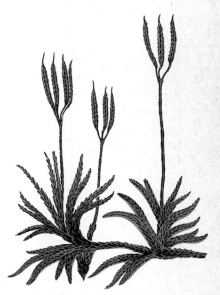

THE CLUB MOSSES, tiny today, give no hint that their extinct forebears were enormous trees. Their miniature leaves twine around their stems in spirals and appear to be moss.

41

Surprisingly enough, modern man has had an opportunity, if not actually to see what a Devonian landscape looked like, at least to examine some of the things which composed it. About a hundred years ago there was a severe flood in upstate New York. Erosion near the town of Gilboa revealed to the astonished eyes of the inhabitants clusters of trees and stumps in fossil form, many of them still standing upright. Some of the trunks were as much as three feet in diameter, and the trees themselves were estimated to have had a maximum height of 40 feet. Fossils of club mosses were also found in this earliest-known forest. But there they grew as slender trees with drooping branches.

The North American continent suffered one of its periodic inundations by the oceans at the end of the Devonian period, about 350 million years ago, and much of the land between the present-day Appalachians and Rockies became a vast, shallow inland sea. Thus began the Carboniferous period, sometimes called the coal age, a paradise for plant growth. The climate in most of the world was uniform, as in the tropics today; rivers from the uplands washed immense amounts of sediment into this sea, forming vast swamplands from whose fertile muck sprang huge forests such as the planet has never seen since. It was a springtime in the history of plants, an unbelievable blossoming and harvest of plenty.

In the coal-age forests giant ancestors of modern horsetails grew with stems a foot thick, forming dense jungles alongside the rivers and the swamps. Some club mosses developed into trees that soared to heights of nearly 130 feet. Today they are shrunk to a pygmy size of only a foot or so—left behind in an eddy in the swift-flowing stream of life, crowded out by the better-adapted coal-age ancestors of the pines. The ferns, however, thrived—most of them as shrubby 10-foot underbrush that covered the forest floor. Here perhaps they occupied a niche in the lower story of the forest, where they had little competition from other plants. As a result there are 10,000 fern species today, compared with about 1,100 club mosses and only 25 horsetail rushes. Insects were unbelievably large—giant cockroaches, and dragonflies with wingspreads well over two feet. They were preyed upon by hosts of spiders and scorpions.

THERE is no doubt that today's immense coal deposits were formed from these giant forests, buried where they grew—although as recently as 60 years ago some scientists were still maintaining that coal was not of plant origin. It is now known that coal has been formed in small quantities ever since vegetation began to grow on the land, although plants were not abundant enough before the Carboniferous period to produce the deep coal beds mined today. There are a few shallow deposits dating from the previous period, the Devonian, but the luxuriant forests of the Carboniferous are the source of almost all the coal that has fueled modern industry.

The conversion of plants into coal occurs when vegetation does not decay, as dead plants ordinarily do. On a forest floor that has not been flooded with water, insects can get at a fallen tree and bacteria and fungi do their work of breaking it down with the aid of the oxygen that is in the soil. But if the forest becomes a swamp of standing water, then when a tree falls it sinks into mud where there is not enough oxygen for the agents of decay to rot it. Instead, it slowly begins to turn into peat. This happens everywhere that standing water and large amounts of vegetation occur

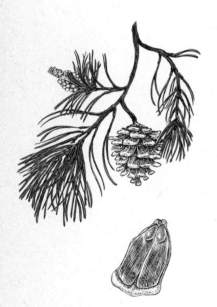

GYMNOSPERMS, including the conifers, produce their seeds on sticky cone scales (*see detail*). They were the earliest plants to develop wind-borne pollen for dispersal of sperm.

together. Peat is being formed today in Ireland, in the Florida Everglades and in the bogs of Canada.

Peat will lie in bogs for thousands of years without changing much. But in time, the shifting of the seas and the sediment carried into the swamps by rivers bury peat deeper and deeper and compress it into lignite, a low-grade coal. Under the weight of millions of years of additional deposits, the lignite is further compacted into bituminous, or "soft" coal. The amount of compression needed is tremendous, for one foot of bituminous coal represents 20 feet of original plant matter. Finally, even additional pressure brought about by shifts in the earth's mantle of rocks compresses the material in many places into anthracite, or "hard" coal. The extent and luxuriance of these Carboniferous forests are demonstrated by coal seams in China that are upward of 400 feet thick—representing an 8,000-foot pile of original vegetation. In Pennsylvania and Ohio, the seams are only five or six feet thick, but they blanket thousands of square miles. Forest flourished on top of previous forest and each in its turn became compacted into a layer of coal. One West Virginia coal bed has been uncovered with 120 such seams, one above the other.

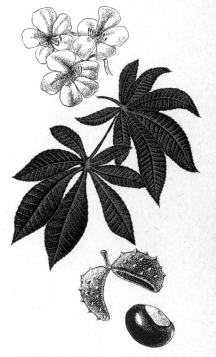

ANGIOSPERMS, such as this horse chestnut, have flowers that attract insects for aid in pollination. Their seeds are always surrounded by a hard or fleshy protective coating.

THE great Carboniferous forests spread over much of the world and lasted through 65 million years of stable climate. But climate, their creator, also brought about their downfall. Vast changes began taking place in the earth—uplift of mountains, violent volcanic eruptions, the appearance of deserts and glacial ice spreading even into the tropics. About 230 million years ago the coal jungles were virtually wiped out, and the awesome vegetation was gradually reduced in size to the low plants seen today along a woodland pond. A new era began, which scientists call the Mesozoic. It was characterized by enormous reptiles and the development of vegetation of a more modern aspect.

To the ascendancy now came trees that had grown inconspicuously in the coal forests. These were the seed plants and in this period of great climatic change their method of reproduction held a key to survival, since seeds are largely resistant to drying out and possess the power of dormancy —the ability to delay germination until conditions become favorable for growth. The first trees to experiment successfully with seeds lacked flowers; the seeds arose on structures somewhat similar to leaves and each seed was exposed. These plants are thus known as gymnosperms (from two Greek words meaning "naked seeds"). The familiar gymnosperms of today are the evergreen trees—the pines, spruces, hemlocks, firs and cedars. Most of them have needlelike leaves and bear their naked seeds on the scales of cones. Almost all the conifers remain green throughout the year (well-known exceptions are tamarack and bald cypress); they do shed their leaves, like deciduous trees, but not all at once.

There was a great variety of gymnosperms in the Mesozoic era. Some have continued to prosper, and carpet large portions of the earth today, but many other kinds became extinct along the path of plant evolution or continue tenaciously only as living fossils. The palmlike cycads, that were as abundant in Mesozoic times as tree club mosses and ferns had been in the coal forests, nowadays grow wild only in the tropics and subtropics (one species is native to southern Florida, and a familiar hothouse plant, mistakenly called the sago palm, is actually a cycad). Another living fossil of this era is the ginkgo, or maidenhair tree. Its leaf, growing in the shape of a fan with veins radiating from the base, so clearly does not belong to the modern flora that the ginkgo could not be confused with any other tree in existence. Ginkgos once grew wild over much of the earth, including Greenland, but only a single species survives today. About 250 years ago the ginkgo was discovered in China by European travelers and it has since been widely planted as an ornamental tree throughout much of the range where it once flourished in the wild state. One can glimpse this relic from the age of dinosaurs along the streets of many North American cities, for the ginkgo is one of the few trees in the world that can endure the poisonous soot of the modern metropolis.

DURING the Mesozoic, a green wave of gymnosperms completely dominated the earth. One of the extensive forests that it formed is preserved today as the Petrified Forest of eastern Arizona. The trees that grew there did not resemble present-day pines; they looked more like the monkey puzzle tree, a native of the Southern Hemisphere occasionally found growing in the United States as an ornamental species. This forest contained trees 200 feet tall. It was inhabited by a wide diversity of large reptiles that were the ancestors of still larger dinosaurs to come. There was a crocodilelike creature about 18 feet long, an amphibian related to the modern salamander but almost nine feet long and weighing about 500 pounds, and a 10-foot thecodont armored with five pairs of spikes projecting from its neck. It was a world of great forests flourishing in the uplands and massive reptiles in the lower swamps.

The trees were continuously swept down from the hills by floods and stranded in the lowland swamps. Age after age, the waters brought down their cargo of trees, shearing them of bark, roots and branches on the way. In other locations or at other periods of the earth's history, these great pine ancestors would have simply decayed or slowly turned to coal. What makes this area so remarkable is that the flotsam of these forests was buried by mud containing ash from volcanoes. Volcanic ash contains large amounts of silica, iron and manganese. These minerals were in the water in which the tumbled trunks lay and they permeated the wood, filling the spaces with silica so gradually and delicately that the cell structure of the wood tissue was preserved. This woodpile-turned-to-stone lay buried for millions of years until erosion of the soil above it uncovered the unbelievable display, splashed with brilliant colors from the iron and manganese in the volcanic ash.

By the start of the Cretaceous, the procession of plant life brought forth and perfected a major development—the flowering plants. There has been considerable debate among paleobotanists about the origin of the flowering plants, but it is possible they came about in this way: gymnosperms bore their ovules (eggs) and pollen (sperm) in separate cones or on leaves, and depended on the wind to bring the two together. In the course of time some beetles may have discovered that drops of sap, exuded by the ovules in the female cones, and the pollen in the male cones would serve as food. These beetles would no doubt return regularly to the new sources of food supply, at the same time accidentally transporting pollen to the eggs. For many plants, this represented more efficient and economical cross-pollination than the old way of haphazardly sending out clouds of

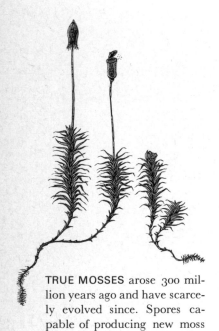

TRUE MOSSES arose 300 million years ago and have scarcely evolved since. Spores capable of producing new moss plants spill into the wind from slender stalked vase structures.

wind-borne pollen. Over a long period of time and through the forces of natural selection, certain plants in all likelihood became sufficiently modified in their structure that they could be said to be adapted to beetle pollination. This meant the development of a continuing supply of sap droplets to attract beetles, and also a means of protecting the eggs so that the beetles could not eat them too. The plants that stumbled along this evolutionary path eventually developed seeds with coats that protected them and are known as angiosperms or "covered seeds." Another adaptation was the attraction of a greater variety of insects by nectar instead of by chance droplets of sap. Also, as more and more insects discovered the new food supply, they brought more pollen and were able to fertilize several eggs at a time rather than just one, making the process even more efficient than the old dependence on wind pollination.

Whatever the exact sequence of events, many flowering trees which arose then are still familiar in the modern landscape: poplars and sassafras, magnolias and willows, sycamores and maples. In the wake of the trees, herbaceous plants developed seed vessels also, and the angiosperms began to colonize the globe. Now they grow practically everywhere that life can exist—from above timber line on the highest mountains to below sea level; in the dry interiors of continents; in swamps and occasionally in salt water. They grow in the form of trees, shrubs, herbs and grasses; directly or indirectly they supply almost all of man's food; they exist in about 250,000 species, magnificent new designs that have added to the world a bounty of flowers, fruits, nuts and almost endless leaf shapes. By the end of the Mesozoic an unprecedented diversity of plant life had evolved on earth.

THE GINKGO, or maidenhair tree, is a relic of the Mesozoic era that grows today in city parks and streets. Its fanlike, veined leaves are unlike those of any other existing plants.

THIS dawn of flowering plants was followed by the birth of other forms that are familiar today. A whole new world of wildlife flocked to the banner of the angiosperm revolution, a world of hummingbirds and butterflies and bees that gathered the nectar of the woods and pollinated the flowers. Mammals ate the fruit in which seeds were enclosed and thus distributed the seeds to sprout in new areas. Along with these harvesters of the forest abundance came the predators that feed upon them, making for the complex food relationships to be found in a modern forest. With the profusion of life that followed the advent of the encased seed, the stage was set for the appearance of "modern" forests on the surface of the earth.

Soon after the start of the Cenozoic era, about 40 million years ago, the planet began to get increasingly colder; the great forests that had prospered inside the Arctic Circle slowly were forced southward. Then, about a million years ago, a monumental event occurred that did much to mold the present pattern of world forests. In North America, the first of four successive ice sheets spread from a radiating point in the Hudson Bay region and reached as far south as New Jersey and Nebraska; other ice sheets similarly blanketed northern Europe and Asia. Like immense bulldozers, these glaciers buried forests where they grew. But as the ice slowly pushed southward, trees in its path continued to scatter seed. Seeds that fell to the north, on frozen ground, perished—but those that were carried southward germinated and built new forests. The pattern of the great arctic forests that had made a luxuriant Eden of Greenland and Alaska was ripped apart. The scattered remnants survived in new locations with new neighbors farther south; many species were locally exterminated.

Before the ice ages, the forests of Europe and North America contained approximately the same kinds of trees. But the ice changed that: today there is not a single native species common to both continents. That is because as the European trees were pushed southward by the ice, they finally came up against east-west mountain barriers that blocked their path—the Alps, Pyrenees, Balkans, Caucasus and other ranges. Since these mountains were already frigid because of their high altitude, seeds of the retreating trees did not lodge where they could grow; with their backs to the wall, almost all the pre-ice age species perished from northern Europe. In North America the situation was entirely different. The great mountain ranges here run north and south, and thus presented no barrier to the retreating forests.

Four times the ice advanced and then retreated. It departed from New England for the last time only about 10,000 years ago, and the world today is probably living in another interglacial period. As the ice retreated, it left behind a land scraped clear of life, its contours changed, debris piled high in some places, swept away in others. It was this flayed skeleton of the earth that the plants set about reclaiming almost immediately.

Now the plants spread north again and the denuded lands saw a procession of life similar to the progress of vegetation through the ages of evolution. In the vanguard were the algae and fungi, followed by plants that could survive in the swamps left by the melting ice—mosses, lichens and horsetails, liverworts and ferns. With them also went some of the hardier herbs, the little plants that need only a thin veneer of soil to grow in, a sprinkling of nutrients to nourish them. In the wake of the glaciers, they formed low-lying plant communities similar to the growth on the arctic barrens today. Behind these pioneers, as the ice continued to melt, marched the gymnosperms of present-day north woods, such as spruce, fir, tamarack and pine. The deciduous trees, though undisturbed by the actual glaciers, had been forced southward by the cold climate. They, too, spread northward again behind the gymnosperms. The rapidity with which vegetation reclothed the land can be seen by the fact that in the 10,000 years since the ice left, the deciduous trees have already gained possession of much of New England. These belts of vegetation are still on the move as the planet continues to warm, particularly in the northern latitudes; in the last several decades alone the coniferous forest has advanced, in some places in Canada, two miles farther north into the tundra.

THE climatic upheaval of the last million years, combined with the improvements in plant fertility of the encased seed and other factors, has made the angiosperms the most successful forms of plant life on the planet today. Vast forests of gymnosperms still flourish around the world, and some of the largest trees on the globe are gymnosperms—sequoias, redwoods, Douglas firs. But coniferous forests today generally inhabit sites unfavorable for the growth of deciduous trees—wind-swept ocean shores, near timberline on mountains, sandy soil in the southern states and the thin soil layer of Canada. Conifers are still widespread, but they have relinquished their hold on the best sites that their ancestors obtained as early seed trees. Today only about 450 species of conifers survive and some botanists speculate that they may be traveling the path to near-oblivion already taken by other gymnosperms, the cycads and ginkgos.

PETRIFIED LOGS IN ARIZONA, 200 MILLION YEARS OLD, WERE TURNED TO STONE BY SILICA IN VOLCANIC ASH THAT BURIED THEM

The Fossil Record

Layers of stone formed in past ages contain the fossils of forests long vanished from the earth. They tell the history of vegetation, from the first land plants to those of more recent times. Plant fossils have been discovered where the earth has been opened by quarries, tunnels, rockslides and coal seams. Occasionally erosion will reveal a magnificent specimen like that shown above.

Life Lines of Plant Evolution

The first plants are believed to have been minute organisms which came into being in the sea. This probably happened two billion years ago and was followed by a long period of evolution, during which marine plants developed many forms but not a single plant appeared on land. It took an astonishingly long time—perhaps as long as 1,400,000,000 years—for the blue-green algae to establish themselves partly on land and partly in the water. From them all other land plants have evolved. An uncounted number have become extinct along the way, but the course of evolution is in the direction of an ever-expanding number of increasingly complex forms. Today there are an estimated 400,000 different species of plants living on the earth.

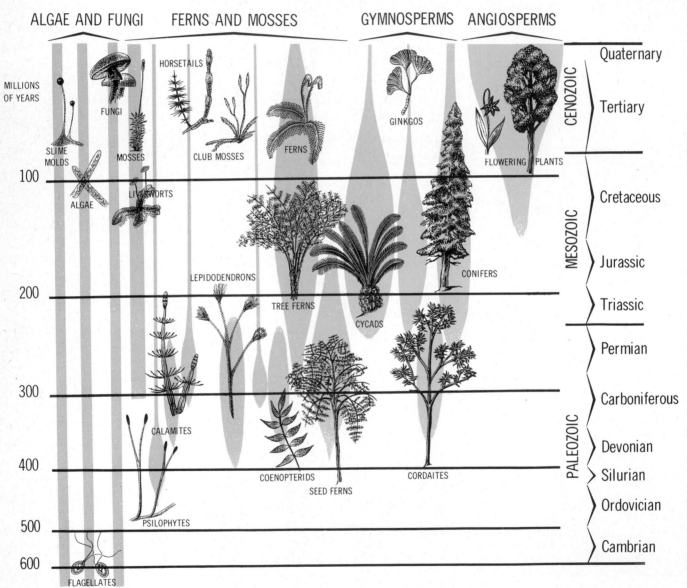

RISE AND FALL of the main types of land vegetation are shown here. Each green column represents a major plant group; the width of the column indicates the abundance of that group at a particular period. Thus, cycads appeared a little over 200 million years ago, flourished for about 100 million years and are now almost extinct, whereas the flowering plants at far right, a recently evolved group, now account for the great bulk of living species. The reason the columns of primitive forms at the left do not swell and shrink is that the plants themselves are small and delicate and do not leave enough in the way of fossils for accurate estimates to be made of their former abundance.

THE WORLD'S FIRST GREEN LANDSCAPE probably looked like this—a few primitive plants, not unlike the seaweeds from which they sprang, growing in or near the water in a land which previously was devoid of life. This painting and the ones that follow are based on detailed study of plant fossils, which are widespread throughout ancient rocks.

Shown above is an early Devonian scene of about 400 million years ago. In the foreground are several kinds of psilopsids—the earliest known plants that left the water to live on the land. They were the first to grow strips of woody cells that helped them to stand up. Different portions of their primitive stems served them as roots and as leaves.

AT THE HEIGHT OF THE CARBONIFEROUS AGE, 100 million years later, primitive land plants had evolved into huge forms that dominated the landscape. Above a dense layer of ferns rose lofty, treelike club mosses, such as Sigillaria (*far left*) and the Lepidodendron (*center right*). These were by far the most abundant plant fossils of the coal-age forests. Both had slender, tapering trunks topped with bushy crowns of branches and grasslike leaves that sometimes reached

lengths of three feet. Most of them reproduced asexually by spores, but a few had evolved seedlike organs. Another tree, the Cordaites (*far right*), may have been the ancestor of modern conifers. It had simple seeds, and is the largest known seed plant of its era. Animals without backbones flourished in the coal-age swamps, and the insects reached sizes never since equaled. The Meganeuron (*above left*) was a primitive giant dragonfly with a wingspread of 29 inches.

WITH THE START OF THE PERMIAN, about 280 million years ago, the greatest time of coal formation came to a close. Innumerable plants had flourished in the mild and humid climate, only to topple over and sink into the mud, since their shallow root systems gave them little support. Sediments washed over them and, with increasing pressures, gradually formed the thick coal seams that man is mining today. The forms of these coal-age trees are still preserved in coal beds

as fossils, especially the diamond-shaped leaf scars that circled the Lepidodendron trunks (*far left*) and the vertical scars that run up and down the Sigillarias (*right*). These looked so much like the scales of snakes that coal miners once thought they had found the remains of tremendous reptiles. The lizardlike animal is an Edaphosaurus, a seven-foot primitive reptile with a huge "sail" which paleontologists suspect may have been a temperature regulator.

IN A TERTIARY SWAMP, 20 million years ago, a primitive tapir wanders in a grove of taxodiums, ancestors of the modern bald cypress. The climate was variable in the Tertiary, encouraging the development of deciduous trees—species that could shed leaves in winter and grow new ones the next year. As long as the weather remained changeable (it still is), deciduous trees had an advantage over conifers and have slowly been encroaching on them ever since.

AN EARLY DECIDUOUS FOREST, dating back to 10 million years ago, begins to have the look of a modern tropical grove, with air plants and flowering vines growing in the branches of the trees, and palms standing by the pools. The animals are dinotheres, extinct cousins of elephants but not quite as large. Their tusks grew downward from their lower jaws, probably to help them browse and root for food. The snake at right is a 30-foot extinct python.

3

Green Patterns Around the Earth

OVER the ages green plants have proliferated into endless varieties which have filled almost every conceivable niche on the planet. The weaving of this evolutionary tapestry may appear entirely haphazard, but there is nothing haphazard about the way it now graces the hills and crannies of the earth's surface. Each strand of the forest tapestry has its own set of needs and abilities. Some trees need direct sunlight throughout their lives, others need it only to germinate—and some will not grow in direct sunlight at all. Many forest plants require "sour," or acid, soil, others require soil that is "sweet," or alkaline. Some thrive on competition but some wither when they are put to the test. Today, forests grow on approximately a third of the land surface of the earth. The figure would be considerably higher were it not for man's destruction of forests, almost all of it accomplished in the last few hundred years, a mere sliver of geologic time. Before Pennsylvania was pioneered, a squirrel could have crossed the state without ever having to come down from the trees; today large

57

portions of Pennsylvania are rolling croplands and pastures. But the disappearance of the forests is a temporary, deceiving picture—for when this land is abandoned, even for only a decade or two, it begins to return to its natural wooded state.

Drought and cold are the two principal limiters of forest growth, although other factors such as soil characteristics, the influence of other plants and animals in the forest, even the microorganisms of the soil can be vital. Trees need a frost-free growing period of at least 14 consecutive weeks and a rainfall of 15 or 20 inches a year. Unusual circumstances can modify these limits: in interior Alaska, where precipitation may be only 10 to 12 inches a year, forests grow because the water that does fall is subjected to a very low rate of evaporation. Along the coasts of western Europe and western North America, forests grow far north of their usual latitude because of the warmth brought by ocean currents. Tropical species often spread far beyond the limits of Cancer and Capricorn. Florida, Bermuda, New Zealand and eastern Australia are all washed by warm ocean currents and take on a tropical aspect. On the other hand, although there is sufficient rainfall and a long growing season in many areas of the North American plains and the steppes of south Russia, trees rarely grow there in the wild state, probably because of low humidity. As a general rule, in areas where trees cannot grow because it is too dry, there are grasslands or deserts; where the climate is too cold, there is tundra.

O N a map of the world showing patterns of vegetation, certain forest types seem to form distinct bands around the Northern Hemisphere, arranged approximately according to the prevailing climate. Close to the pole itself there is, of course, no vegetation whatsoever. But gradually, as one moves south away from the region of perpetual ice, a belt is encountered where the soil thaws for a few weeks in summer to a depth of several inches below the surface. This belt is known as the tundra. It extends around the earth, through the northern parts of North America, Europe and Asia, and can support vegetation. Large areas of the tundra are covered by mosses and lichens, and when the summer thaw comes an explosive burst of hardy arctic flowers comes with it. Only a few trees are to be found in this region. They manage to endure the climate by becoming dwarfs: grotesque thickets of alder, birch and willow literally hug the ground and put on their annual growth imperceptibly.

To the south, the tundra merges into a great belt of conifers that grow where temperatures also are often bitter cold but where there is a longer growing season. This great northern forest sweeps like a green deluge around the world, from the fjords of Norway across Russia to Siberia, then leaping the Bering Strait and carpeting much of Canada all the way to the Atlantic. It consists largely of several species of spruce, but also of pine, fir, hemlock and cedar, with some birch and willow from the tundra mixed with them. This belt is known as the taiga—originally derived from a Russian word meaning "swamp forest" because when the snow melted in early summer in these Russian forests they were inundated by water.

Along its southern edge the belt of dark evergreens merges in its turn into another world-wide tree belt of a different kind: the great Temperate Zone deciduous forest of the eastern United States, the British Isles, central Europe and eastern Asia. These are the familiar woods of western

WORLD FOREST AREAS

(First column of figures shows forested area in millions of acres. Second shows per cent of total land area in forest.)

Europe	348	30
U.S.S.R.	2,795	51
North America	1,811	39
Central America	183	27
South America	2,365	54
Africa	1,861	25
Asia	1,285	19
Pacific Area	237	11

civilization, the ever-changing forests of oak, beech and maple—Sherwood Forest in England, the once magnificent German forest east of the Rhine, which the Roman legions were able to penetrate only intermittently, and the forest of the New England poets. Today this vast domain is occupied by farms and forests of lesser stature, for these primeval woods have been so relentlessly cleared by man that only occasionally do patches survive in the unspoiled state.

Ringing the globe around its midriff is a fourth major belt—the tropical forests. These are of several kinds. Covering the perpetually warm, humid lowlands are the rain forests, which reach their greatest development in the New World but which also form a large wet patch in the heart of Africa and cover parts of India, southeast Asia and Australia. Here is an empire of broad-leaved trees that remain evergreen because of the year-long growing season—teak, mahogany and ebony—a world of exuberant vegetation where immense trees drip with moisture and life seems to overflow. In addition to the rain forest there is the so-called "winter" forest with alternating rainy and dry periods so clear-cut that the trees shed their leaves at the beginning of the dry (or "winter") season and grow them again during the rainy "summer." There are gallery forests which exist as green ribbons that follow waterways into the dry grasslands, grasslands interspersed with scattered islands of trees and shrubs. All these tropical forests have in common an almost constant length of day and night throughout the year and a more abundant and reliable rainfall than is found in other latitudes.

These global bands of native vegetation contain a remarkable diversity of subzones and transitional forests. Committees of the Society of American Foresters have recognized 147 distinct forest types in the U.S. alone, containing different combinations of 1,182 species of trees. To trace out each of the different kinds on every continent would require a vegetation map that resembled a patchwork quilt. Intricate as were the boundaries of the primeval forests, man's intrusions with logging, fire and reforestation have mixed them up even more. Lebanon was covered with great cedar forests 3,000 years ago, and dense forests once flourished in now-scrubby areas of Spain, southern France, Turkey and Greece.

NORTH AMERICA is mantled with such a wide variety of forests that few people can claim to have seen every one of the different kinds of North American trees, much less identify them all at sight. Unfurled like a green ribbon down the West Coast from Alaska to California is a coniferous forest that cannot be equaled anywhere in the world. It includes the largest trees in the world—redwoods and Douglas fir, plus lesser giants like Sitka spruce and western red cedar. Running parallel to it 800 miles to the east is another forest of coniferous giants that seem small only by comparison: it covers the Rocky Mountains from Canada to Mexico with sturdy columns of ponderosa pine, Engelmann spruce, white fir and larch. And framing the roof of North America—from ocean to ocean and sending feelers through New England down the rampart of the Appalachian Mountains—is an evergreen band made up mainly of spruces, very nearly black against the sky, and balsam fir with its sweet incense. With them are their intimate associates, hemlock, pine and northern white cedar as well as several deciduous trees such as birch and sugar maple. It is in the southern

U.S. FOREST AREAS

(First column of figures shows forested area in thousands of acres. Second shows per cent of total land area in forest.)

Alabama	20,771	63
Alaska	136,208	36
Arizona	19,212	26
Arkansas	20,816	61
California	42,541	42
Colorado	20,834	31
Connecticut	1,990	62
Delaware	392	29
Florida	21,016	56
Georgia	24,057	64
Hawaii	2,000	49
Idaho	21,025	39
Illinois	3,993	11
Indiana	4,103	18
Iowa	2,620	7
Kansas	1,668	2
Kentucky	11,497	44
Louisiana	16,129	52
Maine	17,425	82
Maryland	2,920	43
Massachusetts	3,288	62
Michigan	19,699	53
Minnesota	19,344	36
Mississippi	17,225	57
Missouri	15,177	34
Montana	22,330	24
Nebraska	1,482	3
Nevada	12,036	17
New Hampshire	4,848	81
New Jersey	2,229	44
New Mexico	21,329	27
New York	14,450	46
North Carolina	20,076	59
North Dakota	467	1
Ohio	5,446	21
Oklahoma	10,051	22
Oregon	30,261	49
Pennsylvania	15,186	52
Rhode Island	434	56
South Carolina	12,016	60
South Dakota	2,169	4
Tennessee	12,558	47
Texas	37,656	22
Utah	16,219	30
Vermont	3,730	72
Virginia	16,114	62
Washington	23,868	55
West Virginia	9,907	44
Wisconsin	15,588	43
Wyoming	10,513	17

portions of this forest that the magnificent white pine once grew to 200 feet, putting out its branches in tiers like a Chinese pagoda.

Covering almost the entire eastern half of the United States is the great deciduous forest area that stretches from the Atlantic Ocean west beyond the Mississippi River, snaking deep into the dry prairies, following stream courses almost to the Rockies themselves. Most of the original forest that grew here has been logged over many times and supplanted by farms and cities; yet scattered throughout this immense area are occasional remains of the primeval growth.

North America includes other forests of lesser extent. On the sandy soils of the drab Atlantic coastal plain flourish the straight columns of the southern pines—pitch, shortleaf, loblolly, longleaf and slash. At the southern tip of Florida and in a sliver of Texas is what some botanists consider to be the only tropical forest on the continental United States. Here is a little world of trees that have the ring of the jungle in their names—gumbo limbos, blollies, tamarinds, wild mahogany and poisonwood.

In the foothills of southern California there is a heavy rainfall during the winter, followed by a long dry summer and autumn. Although there is enough water—on the annual average—to support luxuriant growth, little of this water is available during the growing season. The forests that result consist of dry, leathery leaved shrubs, known as chaparral, more characteristic of deserts. At the edges of the great southwestern deserts are other areas of scrub vegetation, mesquite forests—and the saguaro cactus forest of southern Arizona and northern Mexico, once described as "a wilderness of unreality." Here, like fantastic candelabra nearly 50 feet high, grow specimens that may weigh 10 tons, mostly water, and put out dozens of branches that twist and bend grotesquely like beckoning arms. Donald Culross Peattie once summarized a saguaro as "a tree designed by someone who had never seen a tree."

IN addition to the east-west belt pattern imposed on North American forests by the climate, their design is affected by the continent's massive north-south mountain barriers. On the United States West Coast, the winds that sweep landward from the Pacific are heavy with moisture. As they meet the slopes of the coast ranges that form the western rim of the continent, they are forced to rise abruptly and cool. Their moisture condenses and they drop more than 12 feet of rain and snow a year in some places, producing the West Coast coniferous belt. Their moisture wrung out, the dry winds continue across the lands between the Sierra Nevada Mountains of California and the Rockies, causing semi-arid conditions where trees cannot grow. Gradually the winds accumulate additional moisture and, reaching the Rockies, they are forced to rise once more; they again drop their cargo of water and account for another north-south forest belt. Depleted of moisture now, the winds fail to water the vast heartland of North America east of the Rockies and as a result it is a dry plain. Toward the Mississippi River, the grasses are taller and more luxuriant as the result of the humidifying effect of the Great Lakes and Gulf of Mexico, and form the prairie which gradually merges into the forests that blanket the eastern United States.

The forest pattern is also influenced by altitude. As one climbs a high peak the air becomes increasingly colder, the wind blows stronger and

THE SAGUARO CACTUS has a fluted surface with deep vertical ridges. Like an accordion, it expands during the brief desert rainy season as it stores up water and grows green and plump.

there are striking alterations in the kinds of plants that grow on the slopes. In fact, tree species seem to drape themselves into distinct horizontal zones around mountains—and an observer would see the same procession of zones if, instead of climbing, he traveled northward at sea level. Each 1,000 feet in ascent of a mountain is equivalent to a trip of 300 miles northward; that is why the top of a high mountain on the equator contains plants and animals similar in their adaptations to those found in the Arctic lowlands.

The way in which forests arrange themselves in bands around a mountain can best be seen on an automobile drive up one of the high mountain passes in the Rockies. The trip begins from the base of the Rockies, about 4,000 feet above sea level, where the vegetation is sparse—sagebrush, short grasses and wild flowers, adapted to survive in this zone of scant rainfall and high evaporation rates. As the road winds up the mountain out of the dry plain, a few low-growing trees begin to make their appearance—willows, alders and little piñon pines that cling to the sun-baked hills. At roughly 6,000 feet one enters the Transition zone: rainfall increases and more trees grow, far apart at first, then in groves of juniper and ponderosa pine with its long needles and golden trunks. The Montane zone is reached at 8,000 feet and the scenery changes once again—from the open-spaced ponderosa pine resembling trees planted in a park, to dense stands of black-green Douglas fir growing tightly together and thereby receiving mutual protection from the increasing winds. Their root systems are shallower than those of the pines in the zone just below and they can better grow in the thin mountain soil. Also the tapering lances of their slender tops offer less resistance to the whipping of the wind than the heavy-topped pines. At about 10,000 feet the traveler reaches the Subalpine zone, also called the Hudsonian because of the similarity of its climate to that of Hudson Bay in northern Canada. The Douglas fir rapidly disappears, replaced by tall narrow Englemann spruce and alpine fir.

The frontier above which trees cannot grow—called the timber line—is at approximately 11,500 feet and marks the beginning of the Alpine zone. There, the trees appear to surrender unwillingly to the severe climate; they become twisted dwarfs before the sweeping gales, growing only as low bushes or vines pressed against the rocks. Here are whole forests of little willows, spruce and fir that may reach only to the ankle, yet number their age in the scores of years. Finally, even they cannot withstand the blasts of cold and desiccating winds, and the mountain heights are clothed only by mats of little plants that live their brief existences in spoonfuls of soil caught in the crevices between rocks. At the topmost peaks even these disappear; in the land of snows that linger over the summer the entire plant kingdom has but a sole representative—a thin crust of lichens on the boulders.

WHENEVER a forest is examined closely, there can be found crosscurrents of temperature, moisture, slope and many other factors—all of which determine where trees can or cannot grow. Yet forests are never standing still. The pattern of trees on the land alters with each shift—a major shift in the case of changes in the crust of the earth or climate, minor and almost imperceptible in regard to alterations in surrounding vegetation. Each kind of forest is actually a living community which has its own laws and a governing body of the dominant plants and animals, and each goes through a period of infancy, youth, maturity and old age.

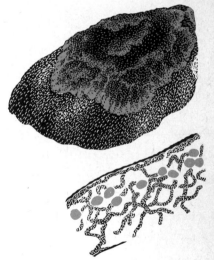

LICHENS are hardy organisms that can flourish on bare antarctic rock. Each lichen, as the diagram shows, combines an alga (green) and a threadlike fungus living together as one.

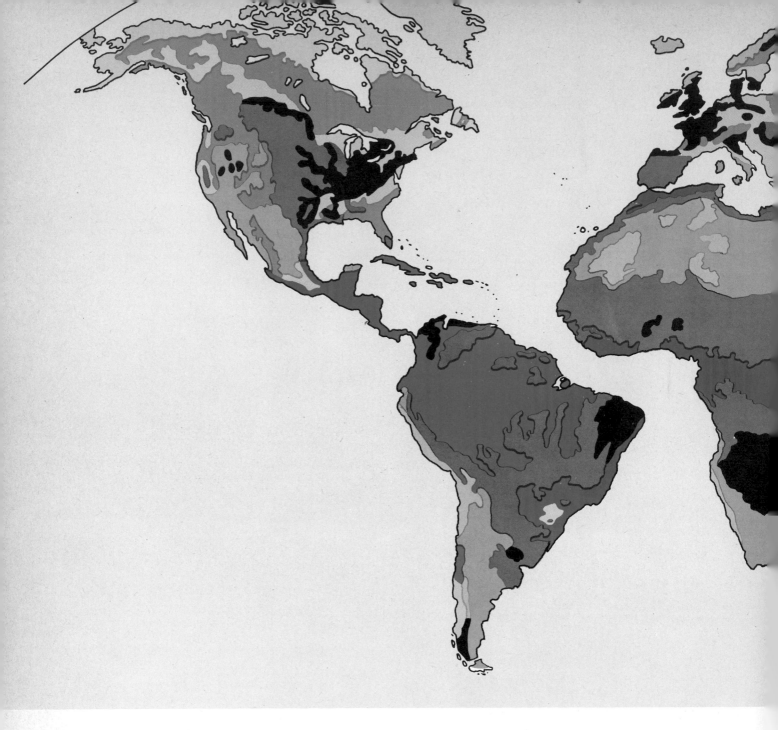

MIXED FOREST covers large parts of the eastern United States, central Europe and eastern Asia. Here tall evergreen trees like the hemlock are interspersed with such deciduous tree species as oak, beech and maple.

NEEDLE-LEAF DECIDUOUS trees are found in the largest stands in the intensely cold regions of northern Asia, where the graceful larch is the main species. These trees have needles but drop them in the autumn.

NEEDLE-LEAF EVERGREENS include the sturdy forests of pine, fir and spruce which cover the far north, creep high in the mountains of most latitudes and thrive in the poor soil of areas like the southeast United States.

BROADLEAF EVERGREENS make up the main growth of the tropical areas commonly called rain forest and jungle. Pampered by constant warmth and abundant water, they hold their lush green leaves the year round.

BARRENLANDS include the icecaps; the deserts of the middle latitudes, where vegetation is sparse; and also the vast frozen deserts of the North, the tundra, where the ground is covered by a mat of small plants.

SHRUBLANDS occur primarily in semi-arid areas, mostly in the tropic regions. Shrubs are woody—like trees—but instead of having a central trunk they generally branch directly from the ground. They are usually small.

GRASSLANDS cover immense areas of earth, generally in regions of moderate rainfall. Clearing by man and grazing by animals have converted into grassland many large areas of the world that were originally forested.

BROADLEAF DECIDUOUS trees like oak, elm and ash which shed their leaves each fall are the common species of the Temperate Zone. Deciduous trees also live in the tropics and shed leaves during the dry seasons.

Forest Empires

The globe is patterned with the provinces of the evergreen and the deciduous, the mighty and the frail. Each, as shown on the vegetation map above, has its established kingdom irrespective of continent. Climate draws the borders of every domain as does the soil and available water. Yet even the harshest environments on earth make a home for some sturdy form of plant life.

THE OLDEST LIVING THINGS are plants, and among the oldest plants are bristlecone pines. Shown here is a specimen growing in the White Mountains of California. It sprouted more than 4,000 years ago, while Egypt's great pyramids were being built. Its main trunk is long dead but it is still slowly putting out some small branches around its base.

THE SNOW-COATED SPIRES OF ALPINE FIRS BOW IN A WINTER GALE ON THE WIND-SWEPT SLOPES OF MOUNT SPOKANE, WASHINGTON

The Retreat of the Conifers

The earth's great coniferous forests are slowly moving northward as the climate becomes milder. Moving in behind them are the deciduous trees, which are better adapted to infiltrate and dominate the warmer habitats that the conifers once ruled as their own. Vast forests of conifers still exist—pine, spruce, hemlock—and they cover enormous expanses of the Northern Hemisphere, but these are in less favorable areas where deciduous trees cannot compete; the climate is cold, dry and windy, and the soil is generally poor and sandy. There are about 450 living species of conifers, but only a relatively few of them are lowland inhabitants. The hardy species shown here, and others like them, can cling tenaciously to life in harsh environments, growing extremely slowly in gnarled shapes, some of them (*opposite page*) having tremendously long lives.

BEATEN TO EARTH by subarctic winds, a stunted spruce grows flat on the ground in a barren area lying between forest line and tundra in Canada's Northwest Territories.

TIMBER LINE is marked by spruce and limber pine (*right*) in Utah's Manti National Forest. Such dwarfed trees are called *Krummholz*, the German word for "crooked wood."

Monarchs of the Forest, the Giant Sequoias

The world's most massive living things are California's giant sequoias, found on the western slopes of the Sierra Nevadas at altitudes from 4,500 to 8,000 feet. They do not grow as tall as another type of sequoia, the coast redwood, which inhabits foggy areas near the sea, but their trunks are much thicker and their total bulk greater. For example, the General Grant tree at right contains sufficient wood to build a village of 50 six-room houses.

Sequoias live upward of 3,000 years and, next to the bristlecone pines, are among the oldest of living things. Their longevity is largely due to the extraordinary qualities of sequoia bark. It is too thick (sometimes up to two feet) and too highly flavored with tannin to be vulnerable to attack by any known species of insect. Spongy and fibrous, it is nearly as fireproof as asbestos. The top of one sequoia, struck by lightning a few years ago during a July thunderstorm, smoldered quietly, without apparently damaging the tree, until it was put out by a snowstorm in October. About the only things that can threaten a mature sequoia are a change of climate, earth-

quakes and erosion. These latter two causes might upset the balance of the tree and cause it to topple. But even this is unlikely; a sequoia's great flat mat of roots covers three or four acres. A giant sequoia may begin to bear seeds at 70 years of age, but is not usually mature until it is 300 or more years old. Then it rains down millions of seeds with kernels the size of a pinhead. What with the heavy shade cast by their gigantic parent and the matted roots beneath them, these seeds have little chance of maturing. Experts have rated the odds against each seed at about a billion to one. Nevertheless, the trees are well able to reproduce themselves if left alone by man. They were heavily logged in years past. Their wood was found to be attractive, a salmon pink color when first cut, turning to a dark maroon when it weathers. Furthermore, like the bark, the wood of the sequoias is remarkably durable. Fallen trees may lie on the ground for hundreds of years and not show any signs of decay, and the wood burns very slowly since it contains practically no pitch. However, loggers soon found that their huge size made the sequoias hard to transport and, while durable in one way, the wood was brittle and apt to smash when the tree was felled. Now the sequoia is protected and on the increase.

A TITANIC CONIFER (*right*), the General Grant sequoia may be 3,500 years old, is 267.4 feet tall and 40.3 feet in diameter, and is still growing.

UNDER COFFEE-COLORED WATERS, the soil of a cypress swamp is spongy and peatlike. The huge trees, as tall as 120 feet, have buttressed trunks and long thick roots to anchor them in their unstable footing.

Water Supply—Too Much or Too Little

Many trees have adapted marvelously to strange environments, where there may be too much water or hardly any at all. The bald cypress (*above*) stands in water and must grow knee roots above the surface to get air. Another water grower, the mangrove (*below*), needs a precise combination of salty water and silt-laden fresh river water for its life in tidal borderlands. In dry areas, like the parklike savannas of Africa, the acacias (*right*) cannot grow close together. The mature trees have such well developed root systems that they catch all water available in the area.

SHORE-FRINGING MANGROVES (*below*) are washed by the briny tide, lethal to most plants. They conserve fresh water with thick waxy leaves, like desert plants. Their anchoring stilt roots are crusted with oysters.

ELEPHANTS GRAZE IN A CONGO SAVANNA AMONG

ACACIAS WHICH ENDURE NINE-MONTH DROUGHTS BY GROWING HUGE ROOT SYSTEMS. THIS RESULTS IN WIDE SPACING OF TREES

TREE SENECIOS cluster at 13,000 feet on Mount Kilimanjaro in eastern Africa. Durable and deciduous, they grow 20 feet high but are really huge relatives of daisies.

Masqueraders in Tree Form

Tropical vegetation is generally long-lived, woody and treelike in size, but some of its "trees" are simply ferns, grasses and other flowering plants that attain great heights and take on strange shapes. Species closely linked to them occur only as small ground herbs in temperate climates. The giant senecios above, for example, grow tall and stout near the timber line on Kilimanjaro, but they are really members of the aster-daisy-sunflower family.

The Joshua trees, which were named by traveling Mormons to whom they looked like beckoning prophets, also maintain the semblance of true trees. But like the 50-foot ferns at far right, they have no solid wood in their tough, fibrous trunks. The bamboos, on the other hand, not only lack solidity and the growth layers of trees, but they are hollow like most members of the grass family, to which they belong. The bamboos appear in great variety, almost 700 kinds—some only a few inches high, and some giants of 120 feet.

JOSHUA TREES twist their clubbed limbs, bristling with swordlike leaves, on a California desert (*opposite*). In spite of their strange shapes, these 40-foot yuccas are actually lilies.

BAMBOO STALKS form a grove (*below*) in China. This jointed plant, while looking like a tree, is simply a fast-growing, gigantic grass. Some species can grow three feet in 24 hours.

TREE FERNS lift delicate crowns on a volcanic height in Java. In this rainy, humid home they may grow as tall as a six-story building. But their trunks remain slender and their leaves uncoil from a fiddlehead, just as do those of their smaller woodland relatives.

THE JUNGLE'S FACE is a wall
of dense foliage garlanded with
hanging lianas. It is best seen
from a river or a small clearing, as in this picture of the
South American rain forest.

4

From Jungle to North Woods

Each time one enters a forest one has a feeling of having been there before. No matter where the forest is located or the kinds of trees that make it up, there is a powerful awareness of its kinship with others around the globe. Forests are bound together by a common thread—the profusion of ways in which they manage to construct communities of life under varying realities of existence. Yet each possesses an organization all its own, and remains vivid and separate in the recollection of the visitor.

One such memorable place is the tropical rain forest of Central America. When one penetrates behind its green facade, he finds himself in a maze of unbranching trunks that soar upward, their crowns indistinguishable among the high latticework of foliage. Lianas or woody vines, some as thick as a man's body, hang like cables. The trees appear to bear a multitude of flowers, but few of the blossoms are their own; most belong to the aerial plants that perch by the thousands on the branches, wafting a heavy fragrance through the forest when the wind blows suddenly.

The storybook "jungle" that must be hacked through by a traveler is only found in a rain forest that has been disturbed by man or that borders stream courses and forest margins where sunlight produces rank growth. In undisturbed rain forests, the canopy of leaves is so thick that even in the middle of the day the light is reminiscent of Temperate Zone twilight. This scarcity of light suppresses most of the undergrowth. As a result, between the colonnades of the trunks the forest aisles are comparatively open. Nor is the ground heaped high with rotting vegetation, as is usually imagined; rather the visitor walks on bare patches of clay soil or on thin layers of leaves that flutter down throughout the year. It requires only a few weeks for a fallen branch to vanish, quickly decomposed by the teeming fungi, bacteria and insects. "Soil," as a gardener knows it, is practically non-existent in the tropical rain forest; little humus accumulates and the steady fall of moisture leaches out minerals. Amazingly enough, the abundant rain forest is erected on a foundation of impoverished soil.

MORE than in any other forest on earth, the impression of wood is overwhelming. Not only are individual tree trunks enormous; even the climbing plants that hang from the branches are like trees themselves, and a large proportion of the undergrowth is also woody. Many of the families of plants that residents of the Temperate Zone know as insignificant ground-hugging herbs here grow to immense size. "Verbena" is a spreading tree with leaves like a horse chestnut; there are "violets" the size of apple trees; "milkworts" flourish as stout twiners that climb to the tops of the highest trees more than a hundred feet above the ground and there bloom. Even some of the grasses—such as bamboo—are woody and may grow to a height of 120 feet.

This is a land where winter never comes, where there is no splendor of fall foliage but only the alternation of a very wet season with one which is "dry" only by comparison. Despite the apparent monotony, when the elements that compose the rain forest are examined closely, it displays an extraordinary beauty and a bewildering variety of life. A survey conducted in a forest in Guyana on a plot of little more than five acres revealed 86 species of trees more than 15 feet high, and the total number of woody species was estimated to be between 150 and 200. On the other hand, there are not many trees of the same kind in a given area. If a visitor becomes intrigued by the magnificence of an *almendro*, for example, and wants to see another specimen, he may look in vain in every direction and not find another one for half a mile.

The organization of most rain forests has been shown to be exceedingly complex. Many of them contain several forests in one—"a forest above a forest," the German naturalist-explorer Humboldt called it. An outstanding example of this layered structure is found on Barro Colorado Island in the Panama Canal Zone, where at least five different tiers can be recognized. Topmost are the clumps of trees that emerge from the main forest canopy to heights of perhaps 125 to 175 feet, and hang over it like green cumulus clouds. The canopy proper is approximately 75 to 100 feet high, and the crowns of these tall trees so interlock that they form a thin mesh that shuts out much of the sunlight. Beneath this layer is one formed by the tops of lower trees, 40 to 60 feet in height, that struggle upward for a glint of light. Farther down is another layer of still smaller trees 20 to 30 feet

FOUR VEGETATION LAYERS in a tropical rain forest struggle for light. Short herbs and young trees are shaded by a dense canopy layer. A few giant "emergent" trees tower above all.

tall, and last of all a shrub layer that rises about 10 feet high and receives scarcely any light at all.

The visitor to a rain forest who expects to see the cup of animal life overflowing will be disappointed if his stay is a brief one. During the day the air is remarkably silent. Only occasionally will he hear the chatter of parrots, macaws and toucans or the cries of invisible monkeys. Insects are the most abundant life of the forest but many remain unseen because of their astounding camouflage. They may resemble animal droppings, leaves, twigs or just debris. A leaf-imitating tropical katydid, for example, has wings complete with fungus spots and imitation dewdrops. There is a grasshopper with leaflike wings, parts of which appear to be eaten away by other insects. Walking sticks half a foot long are decorated with spines tinted red like thorns. Ants are everywhere.

At sundown the oppressive silence is shattered. Flocks of parakeets and gaudy parrots fly screaming to their roosts. Crickets and katydids begin their rasping choruses, joined by many kinds of frogs and toads. Occasionally, howler monkeys set up an earsplitting roar that some have found appealing in the unison of its deep harmonies, but others consider as agonizing as the bellowing of a kennelful of dogs. When it fades, one can hear anonymous rustlings in the foliage as opossums, mice and lizards move through the dark clouds of the canopy or anteaters rip open termite and ant nests. On the ground there are occasional loud snorts as the largest of American rain forest animals, the long-nosed tapirs and the piglike peccaries, push through the darkness.

THE great trees furnish support for much of the other plant life of the forest. Climbers are abundant, much more so than elsewhere. Greedy for light, they have various adaptations for hoisting themselves to the upper canopy—some are twiners, others are equipped with tendrils, hooks or suckers. An entire group of plants is unfitted to start low and climb high to reach the light; they must start high to begin with. These are epiphytes, plants that grow on trees without parasitizing them or deriving any advantage except a platform near the sun. They are extraordinarily common. However, in order to grow close to the sunlight, they have had to pay a price—they have lost their root connection with the forest floor and its abundant moisture. For soil, they must often make do with the small amounts of debris that lodge in crannies in the trees, with dust from the atmosphere and organic matter and seeds deposited by ants that often nest in the roots of epiphytes—a small but vital source of humus and minerals. So well have these plants managed to create their own environment that the spoonfuls of soil in which they grow do not differ significantly from normal soil in microbiological processes.

Some of the epiphytes have developed remarkable adaptations for conserving water. Many are encased in a waxy layer that retards evaporation. The roots of some orchids have a spongy tissue that not only soaks up water but also carries on photosynthesis. The staghorn fern accumulates water-holding humus in a sort of bucket structure at the base of its leaves. The large group of tropical plants known as bromeliads are living cisterns —their long branching leaves spring from the same place around the stem, and overlap so tightly at their bases that they can hold water, as much as four-and-a-half quarts in a large plant. These bromeliad tanks become a center of life, holding breeding frogs, snails and aquatic insects, all of which add to the supply of nutrients in the water. Hairs at the base of the leaves line the tank and perform the job of absorbing water and nutrients, making the bromeliad independent of a root connection with the soil.

The problems of living in the dark rain forest, and the unusual efforts made to rise into the sun, are best symbolized by the strangler trees. They achieve their place in the sun by stealth. The strangler begins life as an epiphyte, its seed germinating high up in a fork of a large tree. The seedling puts out two kinds of roots: one seizes the branch and serves as a grapple to hold the plant in place, and the other dangles like a cable, growing steadily closer to the soil. Until it makes contact with the ground, the strangler grows like any other epiphyte, obtaining small quantities of water and nutrients from the debris in the tree crevice. But once the descending root reaches the soil its source of supply is increased enormously and the plant's growth quickens. It sprouts more leaves high in the canopy and grows upward toward a sunlit window between the leaves; a maze of additional feeding cables descends to the soil and eventually the supporting tree is encased in a network of them. It was once thought that the strangler kills the forest giant by the simple process of enwrapping it and preventing its trunk from expanding, but it is now known that it actually squeezes its host to death. As the hold tightens, the strangler's roots thicken markedly, preparing for the time when it will need props to stand by itself in the sunlight it has captured. The host finally expires, thoroughly encased inside the "trunk" (actually the fused roots) of the strangler and rots away, leaving in its stead a hollow strangler tree which now stands on its own pedestal as a member of the high forest canopy.

ANOTHER primeval battle is waged between inexorable natural forces in another kind of forest that is found along quiet tropical shores around the world—the mangrove islands. Approaching a mangrove thicket by boat, one cannot escape the feeling that this is the most elemental of all forests, for its tangled, arching roots rise directly out of the salt water. The labyrinth of entwined vegetation makes it one of the most impenetrable forests on earth and a haven for colonies of long-legged, long-necked tropical birds like egrets, ibis, spoonbills and herons that roost on these little islands by the thousands. Great blue herons search in the shallows for food, spoonbills strain invertebrates through their paddle-shaped bills and pelicans crash into their nests among the mangroves.

Here it is possible to see a forest being born step by step, miraculously, out of the nothingness of the sea. First, ocean currents and little coral animals build up a reef or sand bar, but unless it is bound together by a protective blanket of vegetation, it will be scoured by tides and storms and vanish. Few plants can gain a foothold on such a spot and indeed only one tree in the Western Hemisphere thrives under these conditions—the red mangrove. The problems it must deal with are immense: the seedling cast into the ocean must be prepared to endure long periods of immersion in salt water before it reaches a sand bar; once there it must anchor itself. Finally, not only must it endure but it must also create conditions that allow the formation of a community of other plants and animals.

The red mangrove is wondrously adapted to this sort of life. Its seeds need no earth but germinate in fruit that stays on the tree, finally developing

AERIAL CISTERNS, bromeliads get their water from rain and their food from particles borne by the wind. The bark surface of trees that support them offers an additional supply.

into seedlings about a foot long. The long thin tube of each seedling is its trunk, the pointed tip is the beginning of its roots and the soft green upper end is its first branch. At the proper time the seedling drops off the parent tree and is carried by the whims of ocean currents, storing its power of growth until it comes to rest—perhaps on a small tentative sand bar. Its sharp root tip is heavier than the rest of the plant. It hangs down and immediately becomes embedded in the little ridge of sand, shells and corals. From here roots are rapidly put down. This is only its exploratory hold: it then sends out multitudes of prop roots that clutch at the surrounding sand like gnarled fingers. Soon they form a tangled network which acts like a sieve, to catch driftwood, decaying sea life and other debris of the currents. From this debris soil is formed. With its roots in the mud and covered by salt water much of the time, the tree is often deprived of air, but it overcomes this obstacle by sending up special breathing roots that emerge from the mud like bristles.

The pioneering tree has now created a foundation favorable for other seedling mangroves brought to this first hint of an island by the currents; soon the pioneer grows large enough to put out seedlings of its own and many of them take root around it. The more mangroves there are to strain the water, the more soil can accumulate under the trunks—and the more hospitable the islet becomes for the growth of more mangroves. And so the process continues in an ever-widening ring as gradually an island of increasing size is built up.

Many of these islands are transitory, for as the mangroves thrive they sow the seeds of their own destruction. They become rookeries for water birds, hundreds of them on even a speck of an island. The birds excrete guano, a fertilizer so concentrated that it burns and scorches living tree tissue. The continual droppings, day after day and year after year, weaken and then kill the trees; the swirling waters of the tides penetrate farther into the island, leaving it vulnerable to the frequent blasts of hurricanes. Sometimes a small island is nearly wiped clean of vegetation in this way. The great hurricanes of 1935 and 1960 stripped many mangroves of their leaves and left sun-bleached graveyards. But new seedlings are already clutching at the sands and the formation of green-draped islands is beginning once again.

ANOTHER forest, totally unlike the mangrove thickets but also permeated by a feeling of water, runs down the northwest coast of North America from Kodiak Island, Alaska, to northern California. This unique domain—actually a collection of different kinds of coniferous forest—is nurtured by the powerful, moisture-laden winds that blow in from the Pacific Ocean. When the winds reach land, they almost immediately encounter the high barrier of the coastal mountain ranges and are forced to rise abruptly. As they do so they become suddenly cooled, their moisture condensing into rain or snow. In some places on this coast, the mountains wring out more than 12 feet of water in a year—equal to dumping more than two billion gallons on every square mile. The result is a great oddity—a rain forest in the Temperate Zone. Fragments of this great forest can still be seen in their virgin splendor.

The vast fall of water has molded the landscape here—cut deep valleys for rushing streams, created glaciers and jewellike lakes—and sustained an extraordinarily lavish vegetation. Wherever one travels throughout this rainy empire one can see towering columns of dark conifers, their high branches interlocking in such a close web that they shut out the sky. The southern anchor of the rain belt is a narrow, 450-mile-long ribbon, roughly 20 miles wide, where grows the coast redwood, *Sequoia sempervirens*, the "everliving sequoia." It lives close to the sea, never out of reach of the summer fogs that drift in from the ocean, saturating the air and reducing the water loss from the leaves. This species towers above every other kind of tree on earth, the tallest living specimen measuring 367 feet, 9 inches, although some of the trees previously logged here are thought to have been considerably taller. The great pleated columns of the redwoods rise straight and true, with scarcely a taper, for a hundred feet before they erupt in a spray of branches. Many of these branches are larger than the trunks of the biggest trees found in eastern deciduous forests. Their roots, like those of the giant sequoia, form broad shallow mats only a few inches below the surface of the ground. Even walking on them can trample down the soil enough to injure them. One redwood may weigh a thousand tons or more and may be as old as 2,000 years.

THE jewel on this green ribbon, however, is the Olympic rain forest in the state of Washington, an unreal world permeated by a misty aura from water particles that saturate the air. The few roads that penetrate it enable only the narrowest of light shafts to cut through to the floor of this untamed wilderness. Here are dense stands of western hemlock and western red cedar growing 200 feet high and Sitka spruce so great of girth that 10 full-grown men could not join hands around their bases. Where the forest has been disturbed by fire, windstorm or logging grow the gigantic and deeply furrowed trunks of Douglas fir. But they are transitory members of this rain forest, sprouting only when there is sunlight; a sapling of one is rarely seen under the dense shade cast by the hemlocks and spruces.

Beneath these huge trees the forest floor is covered by a dense undergrowth, reminiscent of the storybook "jungles" of the tropics; the weak and sprawling branches of vine maples impede the visitor by forming arches which take root wherever the branch tips fall back to earth. Instead of the tropics' hanging cables of lianas, there are hanging gardens of the moss which upholsters tree trunk, branch and twig alike with a furry blanket for many feet above the ground, carpets fallen timber, coats rocks and makes a sponge of the forest floor so yielding that the visitor sinks in up to his ankles. It hangs in festoons like stage draperies, dividing the forest into galleries, each one more astounding than the last. Even during the constant rain showers, this forest is amazingly silent. Each drop of water that falls is noiselessly soaked up by the moss sponges. The only sounds are the light tinkle of a stream splashing somewhere in its rocky bed or the wind moving the high treetops in a slow groan like timbers straining in a schooner.

Occasionally a giant tree falls to earth or loses one of its tremendous branches. The fallen timber then plays a special role in the economy of this forest. Seedlings of hemlock and spruce have a difficult time getting started because of the thick growth of ground plants. But they can thrive when their seeds lodge on the platform of a rotting log, several feet above the competing vegetation. Thus, fallen wood not only renews the soil but it also acts as a nursery for infant trees. As the saplings grow they put out roots that grope around the perimeter of the decaying log to reach the soil. By the time the fallen tree has completely rotted away, it is straddled by a new giant, seeming to rise from the soil on stilts. This is the reason why the majority of Olympic rain forest trees have swollen bases and often appear to have been placed in rows—rows that follow the decomposed trunks on which they once began life.

A less spectacular but infinitely larger coniferous forest is the north woods, with its endless expanse of spruces stretching their ragged silhouettes against the sky from Alaska eastward across Canada and the northern United States. This vast domain, speckled with myriad lakes and bogs left by the glaciers, is best typified by the black spruce. The black spruce seems to thrive on adversity, for it is found abundantly where the weather is cold and wet and windy, its form sculptured into so many different silhouettes by hardship that its natural shape is hard to determine. Wherever its inky branches weave a latticework against the gray northern sky, they serve as pointers directing the attention of the visitor to the unique community of the northland—the spongy underpinnings of sphagnum moss, the scant undergrowth of Labrador tea and heather, the world of paddling ducks and laughing loons.

Most of the black spruce is made up of dead branches that cling tenaciously to the tree, even after death. Perched atop it are a few feet of green growth, as if the old spruce were tipped with a Christmas tree. Clinging to the old branches are hundreds of cones which the spruce does not yield freely; but when they do finally open, they fill the air with winged seeds which become imbedded in the moss, sometimes so many taking hold that the infant trees completely blanket open areas of a bog, their branches interlacing and forming a thicket a few feet high. Or a seed may enter a fissure in a floating log, sprout and grow there, its roots collecting debris and eventually turning the log into a floating island.

THE black spruce is often accompanied by its more comely sister—the white, which grows tall and true as a mast, its branches and needles curling up at the tips as if they had been combed and groomed. The fibers that make up its trunk are equally dainty: a cubic foot cut from the trunk of a white weighs a mere 25 pounds, compared to 33 pounds for the rugged black. And in these spruce woods will also be found their intimate, the balsam fir, the sweet fragrance of whose needles is packaged and sent to areas where no balsam fir grows.

Spruce and fir inhabit a watery world that was four times bulldozed by glaciers whose destruction can be seen everywhere in the face of the north woods—in dammed-up river courses, in quagmires that form a soggy underpinning for the coniferous forests. Far northern plants and animals have remained in these cold-water lakes despite the retreat of the glaciers. Insulated by layers of peat, existing in a land of long and snowy winters, the bogs have remained too cold for the invasion of southern trees to any great extent. But they are disappearing before the march of the conifers themselves which are filling in the bogs and reclaiming the empire preempted by the glacial water thousands of years ago.

The middle of each bog is a pool of open water, stained clear brown by the peat. Forming a circle around the pool is a bordering ring of low water plants, then another ring of firmer peat and shrub growth. Finally, around that, the spruce and fir take root. Eventually, the knot of trees will tighten and replace the shrubs, then the water plants and the bog will disappear, covered by forest.

The process of filling in the north woods bogs has been continuous since the glaciers departed. Much is known about it, for its story is told in the bottoms of the bogs themselves. When trees became established after the glaciers melted, their rain of pollen settled into the lakes each spring and sank to the bottom; every year a new layer was added on top of the layers of previous years. A bog thus forms a textbook of forest history, each page of which is a thin layer of pollen. Botanists, equipped with long hollow cylinders, can bore to the bottom of the bog and bring up a core that includes samples from all the pages. By studying these cores they can read the clear record of former great forests, changes in the kinds of trees and alterations in climate. Sometimes a bookmark is found among these pages, a black layer, the record of a primeval fire.

IN the same way that the jagged profiles of the black spruce speak for the north woods trees, so do the snowshoe hares for northern animal life. In winter, when all is white on the land, their ceaseless goings and comings lay down tracks that soon grow into broad lanes between the trees and finally into packed highways, as the hares travel from tree to tree to nibble the bark. This is nibbled to exactly the same height on every tree in the forest—marking the highest limit the hares can stretch above the surface of the snow. Hares are a reservoir of food for the hunters of the north woods—foxes and wolves, owls and wolverines. Possibly in no other forest does the food relationship of its inhabitants stand out so plainly: the winter vegetation is mostly in the form of trees which provide food for hares, mice and deer, which in turn provide meat for the hunters. Lumbering porcupines find themselves comfortable perches in the crotches of trees and there feed on twigs, needles and bark.

Beavers year after year add new logs to their dams until they become many feet high and tens of feet long. All around a beaver pond are stumps of trees ending in sharp points where the large incisors of the animals have chiseled them through. The surrounding slopes are roughened and eroded where the beavers have pulled and tugged at the logs, dragging them to the water's edge. Beavers work constantly. As a dam rises, so does the water impounded behind it, and this water finally drowns trees rooted along the shoreline. These are then taken over by woodpeckers, including the largest found in North America, the crow-size pileated with its brilliant red crest. Cavities in the dead trees also provide homes for a number of ducks that nest in them high above the water—wood ducks, hooded mergansers and goldeneyes.

Each of these North American forests—the rainy tropical jungle, the marching mangrove thickets, the fog-belt forests and the north woods—harbors a life that is uniquely its own. Each has its counterpart on other continents with forms of life similar in their adaptations. Yet all are bound together by a common thread, for trees are the pillars upon which the whole structure of forest life is erected. Thus, the tree is actually the architect of other life; different trees create different environments, and in the end dictate the kinds of plants and animals which will live with them.

The Wet, Wild Woods

The Olympic rain forest, unique in North America, is located on a peninsula which juts into the Pacific from the coast of Washington. It is a silent, fog-shrouded area with Indian place names—Hoh, Queets. Its trees are choked with moss and it gets up to 150 inches of rain in a year.

BIGLEAF MAPLES, with leaves up to 15 inches long, stand festooned with mosses and ferns in the Olympic forest.

THE RAIN FOREST FLOOR, from which the trunks of Douglas fir and western hemlock ascend, is dappled by shafts of sunlight and adorned with a profusion of plants. Wood sorrel with its cloverlike leaves grows in the foreground among the mosses. The ferns are western sword ferns, a variety with sharp-pointed, sharp-toothed leaflets that is widely used

in florists' decorations. Fallen rotting trees lie everywhere, some broken from their stumps by gales, others uprooted bodily. Uprooting is fairly common in rain forests. The root systems of some of the biggest trees are shallow, going down only about three feet in the water-soaked soil. By contrast, an oak in a drier forest may send roots down 15 feet.

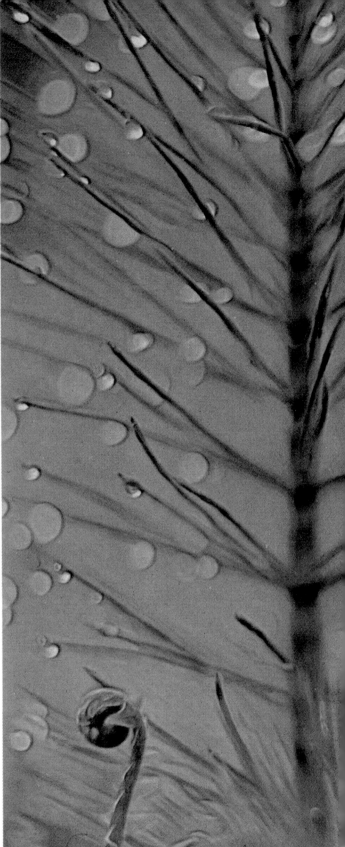

SPARKLING RAINDROPS cling to plants on the forest floor. The uncurling fronds in front are deer ferns, some of which develop a resemblance to antlers and may grow to a height

A VANILLA LEAF (*left*), common on the Pacific Coast, has droplets hanging from all its three parts. It is also known as "sweet-after-death" because of its fragrance when dried.

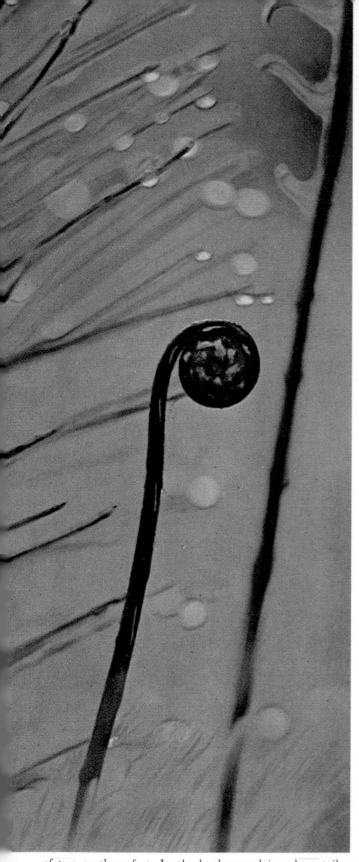

of two or three feet. In the background is a horsetail, a member of one of the most primitive of land plant families, which traces its history back to the Carboniferous period.

SKUNK CABBAGE bears a stalk of fruits (*right*) shielded by a brilliant shell. The plant gets its name from its unpleasant smell. It can melt its way through ice when growing.

LIVING SCULPTURE, the delicately fluted Leucopaxillus mushroom sends its free form arching out of the litter on the forest floor. Mushrooms take their nourishment from decaying matter and help complete its destruction so that it turns into new soil. Thus they play a vital part in the plant cycle.

FROG ON FUNGUS pops its big eyes at the world (*left*). This is a Pacific tree frog with suction discs on its feet that it uses to cling to a smooth surface and to perform acrobatics.

SNAIL ON FERN is a Pacific land snail with eyes in its tentacles, which can be retracted in case of danger. Its foot secretes a sheet of mucus upon which it glides slowly ahead.

SPIDER ON BLOSSOM, a common crab spider (*right*) waits for an unwary insect to come by. These spiders have the ability to change color from white to yellow. Thus they are usually found sitting on white or yellow flowers to camouflage themselves.

DISINTEGRATING LEAF from a red alder lies on a sand pedestal, a mound preserved by the leaf after rain has washed away the earth around it. Decay is fast, with little accumulation of leaf mold or humus as in other Temperate Zone forests.

BURGEONING ROOTS of hemlock feed off a rotting "nurse" log, so-called because it provides the nourishment for new growth. The seedlings cannot compete with ground plants for nourishment from the earth but can survive on decaying logs.

BLIGHTED LEAVES of the bigleaf maple (*left*) are attacked in patches by a fungus. This leaf disease is commonly known as speckled tar spot or black speckled leaf spot. It does not kill trees as more serious blights do but only defaces the leaves.

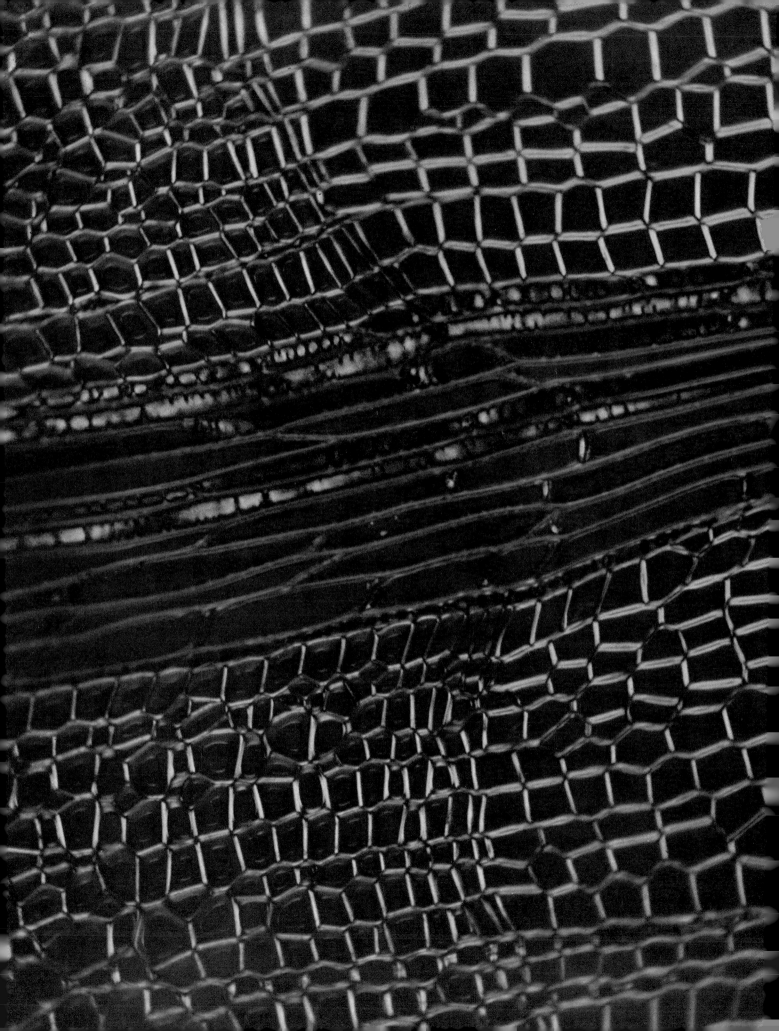

SLICE OF A TRUNK, greatly magnified, shows a "ray" cutting through a honeycomb of wood cells. Small cells at left form in summer; the larger ones, at right, during spring.

5

Tree Engineering

IF someone were to announce that he had invented a machine that was run by energy from the sun, manufactured food out of water and carbon dioxide, was powerful enough to split rock, was not only functional but also extremely beautiful—available in thousands of models, many of which changed colors throughout the year—then people would no doubt travel thousands of miles to gaze upon so wondrous a fabrication. Yet this remarkable mechanism—a tree, any tree—is available for inspection as a common feature of the landscape. Starting as a minute seed, it sometimes grows to heights of over 300 feet, accumulating as much as 50,000 cubic feet of wood in the process, and developing an architecture of soaring trunk and branches on a plan no less grand than that of a Gothic cathedral. In addition, it possesses a plumbing system so ingenious and so powerful that it can raise water about a hundred times as efficiently as the best suction pump ever made.

A tree is constructed solely of cells, the basic units of life. Inside each cell is a nucleus, which carries the chromosomes that guide the development of the tree. The nucleus is suspended in a material with the appearance and consistency of egg white, known as cytoplasm; floating in the cytoplasm are factories for manufacturing substances needed by the cell, warehouses for storing them, little bodies that serve as energy producers, and other structures. The whole complicated speck—perhaps 90 per cent of which is water—is enclosed by a thin membrane and usually a cell wall. From this basic scheme develops a grand variety of growth. A look through a microscope will reveal that the cells in the interior of a leaf are quite different from those in the trunk, and different again from those in the root. Each kind of cell is usually found in association with similar cells; groups of similar cells make up a tissue, and tissues combine into even more complex groupings known as organs.

THAT marvelous organ the root did not exist about 350 million years ago. Early land plants, in their progress from water to soil, apparently first developed underground or creeping stems that performed the functions of anchorage and absorption. From these stems were gradually developed smaller branches that extended into the soil. These in turn were the forerunners of the root systems known today. Roots are often thought of as massive, brown, twisted organs—but those are the older roots and they are composed mostly of nonfunctioning wood. The vital parts of roots, the tips that pry and turn through the soil and absorb vast quantities of water and minerals, are perhaps an inch or so long and thinner than a piece of string. Delicate as these growing tips are, they have been known to probe the earth 40 feet below the soil surface and are attached to the soil grains so tenaciously that they cannot be removed without being broken. Each of the delicate growing tips in a root system, and there may be many millions of them in a single large tree, has a protective cap that fits over it like a thimble; in addition, an oily solution may form around the cap, making it slimy enough to facilitate its burrowing through the soil. The growing tip is like a sensitive probing finger: it veers off when it meets a hard object; in soft earth it penetrates with a corkscrew motion.

The delicate region directly behind the cap is the only place where the root grows in length, pushing the cap ahead of it through the soil. Developing from this section are thousands of tiny white root hairs. Each hair consists of a single cell which has grown at right angles to the root. All of the absorption of water from the soil is performed by these gossamer threads as they attach themselves firmly to the particles of soil. While the hairs are attaching themselves to the soil grains, the root tip pushes forward in the soil, tapping new supplies and giving rise to new root hairs. The older hairs die after a few days or weeks and the section of root in which they sprouted begins to mature. It no longer absorbs. Instead, as it slowly grows thicker with age, it gives increasing support to the tree and conducts water and nutrients to the trunk. Thus, when a gardener waters a tree near its base he is giving the roots only a bath and not a drink; the absorbing parts of the roots are usually some distance from the trunk of the tree, in the area of soil beyond the spread of the outermost branches.

The root system grows steadily, branching and rebranching, constantly putting out more hairs. It would be an impossible task to dig up a large tree and measure its entire root system, but measurements have been made

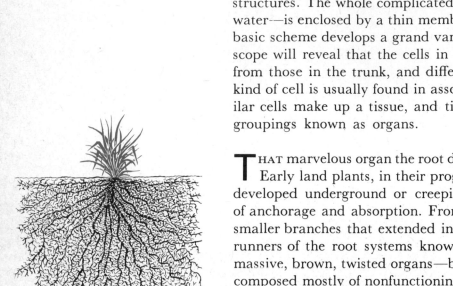

GRASS ROOTS, which may total 400 miles in length, absorb the soil's water and minerals. Each strand of root possesses membranes that control the intake of harmful substances.

of the roots of grasses. Although in these experiments the growing conditions were ideal, and grass roots are of a different form than those of most trees, nevertheless these measurements give an inkling of how far-flung the roots of a tree must be. A single rye plant, after four months of growth, was found to have put out 378 miles of roots, or an average of three miles in a single day. This growth was accomplished by 14 million separate roots which had a total of about 14 billion root hairs.

How much larger the root system of a 100-foot tree is may never be known, but it is clearly a mechanism of almost unbelievable elaborateness. With it the resources of the soil are tapped literally grain by grain in the endless search for water, for trees need water constantly. A single birch may give off through its 200,000 leaves as much as 900 gallons of water in a summer's day. Every drop of this water must be supplied by the delving root hairs, and it is passed along from cell to cell, like buckets of water in a firemen's brigade, until it reaches conducting tissue in the root which carries it up the trunk and to the leaves.

The absorbing portion of the root is a remarkable mechanism. It must take in from the soil minerals essential for the tree's growth, and pass them on to the rest of the living cells in the tree in a continuous stream. The flow has to be one way, for the absorbing cells must also prevent leakage back into the soil of the materials needed by the tree. To complicate the problem, many minerals are harmful to the tree if absorbed in large quantities. Therefore the cells must maintain precise control over the proportion of the different elements taken in. This is accomplished by the presence in each absorbing cell of two membranes which are highly selective: they permit the ready passage of certain elements into the root, but greatly slow down the passage of others.

ROOT TIPS of even large trees are minute but do all of the root's lengthening and probing. Every tip wears a protective cap and has thousands of root hairs to grip the soil.

Besides being an absorbing and conducting structure, roots anchor the tree, a remarkable accomplishment when it is considered that a comparatively thin trunk may grow upward for nearly 100 feet and then become top-heavy in an explosion of branches. The root gains purchase on the soil by branching and rebranching in many directions, pushing its way through the soil grains and packing them firmly against each other. Mature roots maintain their firm pressure against the soil by increasing their diameter, acting somewhat like wedges.

Some root systems are better than others in supporting trees. In one patch of southern New England woods a recent hurricane toppled a number of elms, birches, spruces and hemlocks, all of them species whose root systems extend horizontally close to the soil surface. But the hurricane did not down a single oak, hickory or walnut. These trees have taproots that plumb the earth for support, and are mirror images of the branches and trunk above ground. Each has a central shaft that descends like an inverted trunk, throwing out branches which in turn rebranch, each subbranch carrying its own growing tip. Some tree species, particularly those that grow in dry regions, possess a taproot and surface roots too; the taproot grows deep in the soil, absorbing nutrients and water from a considerable depth and also providing a firm anchorage, while the surface roots collect water and stabilize the tree by acting as guy wires.

In some species, such as mangrove and screw pine, new roots (known as adventitious roots) grow out from the trunk and drop to the ground, lending additional support to the tree. The banyan tree of India, one of many kinds of strangler trees found in the tropics, forms adventitious roots on its branches. These descend as long shoots to the ground where they take hold and increase greatly in size. In this way, a single banyan can spread out tremendous distances, forming pillar after pillar to support the branches. There is a record of a banyan at Calcutta whose main trunk was 42 feet in circumference and which had, in addition, 232 pillar roots, some of them 10 feet in girth.

The competition between trees and other plants to gain possession of an empire of soil has long been known, but it is comparatively recently that scientists have learned that plants attack their neighbors with chemical weapons. A pioneering experiment was performed at the beginning of this century: water that had drained through pots in which grass was growing was used to wet the soil around apple trees growing in tubs. A remarkable slowing down of the growth of the apple trees took place. Farmers have often observed that many plants do not grow in the immediate vicinity of the black walnut; a study of this tree has revealed that it produces a chemical which is toxic to some other plants. When guayule, a large shrub of the dry southwestern United States and Mexico, was grown in a laboratory, its roots were found to give off a substance which inhibited the growth of its own seedlings, a most effective method of eliminating competition for sparse water. So powerful is this substance that even when one part is diluted in 200,000 parts of soil, it is sufficient to inhibit the growth of seedlings. Chemical warfare by plants is such a new study that no one knows exactly its extent, but one authority, James Bonner of the California Institute of Technology, believes it is very widespread: in a survey of woody plants growing in just one section of California, more than half were found to contain substances toxic to other plants.

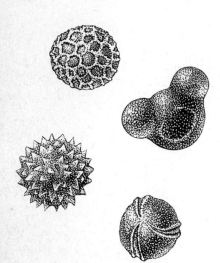

GRAINS OF POLLEN are microscopic, yet each one has a form distinctive to its kind. These are, at top: knotweed (*left*), pitch pine (*right*); at bottom: ragweed (*left*), beech (*right*).

THE most conspicuous part of the tree is its trunk, the member that allows it to rise above the lesser plants of the forest and to dominate all life within reach of its canopy. Each species develops a trunk according to its own inherited pattern. Sometimes this is an unbranched column wearing a crown of leaves at the top, as in most palms and cycads. The great majority of trees, however, follow one of two patterns. Most gymnosperms, including the conifers, have single central trunks rising straight from the ground to the topmost twig. Branches tend to stick out horizontally and get shorter and shorter as they go up. Most angiosperm trees have trunks that divide and redivide into branches. Some trees, such as sugar maple, grow both ways, depending on whether they are crowded in a forest or growing in the open. The branches themselves take many forms—the drooping of weeping willow, the fountain of elm, the rugged horizontal spread of black spruce, the graceful upward arching of the longleaf pine.

The stump of a freshly felled mature tree usually reveals a great dark central area. This looks tougher and less porous than the wood nearer to the bark, and it is, for this is the heartwood, dead tissue whose conducting cells have become clogged with gums and resins. It once transported water and nutrients from the roots to the leaves, when the tree was young and slender, but now the heartwood has been left behind, buried more and more deeply by the rings of new growth around it, and serves primarily as a sturdy support. Only a small part of a tree is alive at any one time, and as it grows and matures it increases not so much with life as by the accumulation of deadwood. A stump two feet in diameter may reveal that all of the tree except for the outer few inches is dead. The tree trunk may be hollow in older trees, its heartwood decayed by fungi and eaten by insects. Despite this the tree functions normally, except that it has lost much of its support and may topple in a strong wind.

SURROUNDING the heartwood are the still-operating cells of the sapwood, usually lighter in color and wet from the countless pipelines that run through it, transporting water and nutrients. Only the outermost ring of cells around the sapwood is still growing. This is the remarkable cambium layer, a sheath only one cell thick that completely encases the wood of the tree from the roots to the topmost twig. This dividing layer of cells builds new conducting tissues—it gives birth both to the wood, or xylem, which conducts water and dissolved minerals upward from the roots, and to the phloem, the tissue to the outside of the cambium which transports and may store food manufactured in the leaves. As a tree begins to renew its growth each spring, the cambium layer splits off rows of daughter cells—those to the inside of the layer forming xylem, those to the outside phloem. The cambium cells bring about growth of the tree only in girth since a tree increases in height solely at the tips of the trunk or branches. This can be proved by a simple experiment: drive a nail into a tree exactly five feet above the ground and come back in several years to inspect it; the nail will still be exactly five feet high.

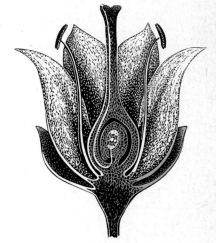

POLLINATION in a flower occurs when a pollen grain lands on top of the vase-shaped female organ. The grain grows a tube to carry the male nucleus to the egg sac inside the flower.

A stump can be clearly seen to be made up of many concentric rings. These are the growth rings, each measuring the amount of wood added to the tree's girth in a year. The most favorable time for tree growth is usually in the spring. Then large tubelike cells with thin walls are formed. This spring wood appears light in color. Later in the season, the cells formed are smaller and thicker-walled, forming a darker band of summer wood. By midsummer the cambium may cease producing xylem entirely. Thus each year the light spring wood grows next to the dense, dark summer wood of the previous year, making a visible line between the growths of successive years. In a temperate climate, a single ring of light and dark wood is usually added each year—but sometimes more than one ring is produced in a growing season, or sometimes no ring at all. For example, if a tree loses most of its leaves from a severe insect attack or drought, it begins producing dense wood and thus completes a ring. Then if a new crop of leaves grows again that same season, stimulating new activity by the cambium, another ring will be formed. In a very dry year the tree might not grow at all and no ring would be added that year. Therefore, counting the rings on a stump does not always give the exact age of the tree. But varying widths of rings tell other facts about its history and about the forest of which it is a part—climatic changes, fires and competition from other trees, all of which alter the formation of annual rings.

A young stem is usually green because chlorophyll in the underlying tissues shows through its covering of transparent protective cells. But after a year or two, the stem is covered by gray or brown outer bark made up of dead phloem and a new tissue, cork, formed by a special layer of cells, the cork cambium. This outer bark of a tree is as dead as its heartwood. As it ages and weathers it becomes ridged and cracked and begins to slough off.

The outer bark of each kind of tree stretches in a characteristic way, so much so that bark is an important aid in identifying trees. Sycamore bark can scarcely stretch at all; it flakes from the stem and branches in large irregular patches, revealing the yellowish or white inner bark. Much of the trunk of a beech, on the other hand, is covered by smoothly stretched bark of a silvery color. White-birch bark peels off like paper. Shagbark-hickory bark resembles shingles on a house. The cork oak of northern Africa and southern Europe puts on a thick uniform layer of bark that can be removed in large sheets to make the many products known as cork. This does not injure the underlying tissues; new layers are produced in a few years which can be similarly harvested.

THE roots, trunk and branches are structures that support and bring raw materials to the leaves, the place in the tree where food is manufactured. Angiosperm trees of the Temperate Zone display a wide variety of leaf shapes—toothed like a buzz saw in elms and pussy willows, lobed in maples and oaks, divided into leaflets like fingers on the palm of a hand in the buckeye. The thin broad leaf of an angiosperm is a most efficient food-manufacturing mechanism: its construction allows a great deal of surface to be exposed to light. The outside of the leaf, top and bottom, is mantled with a transparent layer of cells known as the epidermis. Between the layers of epidermis are cells containing the green substance chlorophyll, and the cells are arranged in such a way as to expose the maximum amount of chlorophyll to the light and at the same time allow circulation of oxygen and carbon dioxide between them.

Running throughout the leaf is an intricate system of veins and veinlets, a continuation of the xylem and phloem pipes of the rest of the tree. These bring in water and nutrients to the leaf and take away the food which it manufactures. If a fresh leaf is held to the light and examined with a magnifying glass, the veinlets can be seen to form such an extensive network through the leaf that no cell is very far from one. All internal cells communicate with the atmosphere through microscopic pores called stomata (from a Greek word meaning "mouths"), usually located on the underside of the leaf. A square inch of leaf may have thousands of them, as many as 35,000 in an inch of oak leaf. Each of the stomata is surrounded by a pair of cells that somewhat resemble lips. These guard cells, as they are called, act like valves to regulate the loss of water by the leaf and the intake and output of gases. An intricate sequence of events opens the stomata during photosynthesis when the water supply is plentiful, and closes them at night and during dry periods.

The leaf is the factory that produces the foodstuffs for the tree's growth and eventually for all the animal life of the forest. As recently as 300 years ago, scientists were mystified about the raw materials used by a tree in its growth. At that time, an inquiring Dutch physician, J. B. van Helmont, performed an ingenious experiment. He planted a willow weighing five pounds in a barrel of soil that weighed exactly 200 pounds. For five years he patiently watered the willow until it had grown into a sizable young tree. He carefully removed the willow and its roots from the barrel—and found that the tree now weighed not five pounds, but 169 pounds, three ounces. When he weighed the soil in the barrel, he was amazed to learn that it had lost a mere two ounces in weight. Obviously the tree's bulk did not come from the soil, except for the two ounces (which it is now known were mineral elements essential for the tree). Somehow, then, the tree was manufacturing its growth out of the water he gave it. Nowadays everyone knows that a green plant takes carbon dioxide from the air and combines it with water in the presence of light to manufacture simple sugars. This chemical reaction takes place in the chlorophyll-containing bodies called chloroplasts, more than a hundred of which may be present in a single photosynthetic cell.

Of the materials the tree uses in photosynthesis, that taken in the greatest amount is water. However, only a small percentage of the water taken in by the tree's roots is retained; most of it is evaporated from the leaves, serving no use and being lost in the atmosphere. People usually regard successful forms of life, such as trees, as being perfectly fitted to their living conditions, all the errors in structure having been eliminated down the long road of evolution. Yet here is a tremendous loss of water that apparently serves no function. It is an unfortunate coincidence for the tree that the best way for photosynthesis to take place is to have wet cell surfaces in contact with the air for the exchange of carbon dioxide and oxygen. This results in constant and tremendous water loss. A tree requires about 55 pounds of water to form 100 pounds of cellulose, the main constituent of wood. Yet, while the tree is making the 100 pounds of wood, it loses in evaporation nearly 1,000 times that weight of water!

To carry the great amounts of water needed to the leaves, a tree is equipped with a circulation system of amazing intricacy that extends from the millions of root hairs through the trunk and branches to the hundreds of thousands of leaves. In the case of the giant sequoia of California, this means that some of the water collected by the roots must travel a distance of nearly 450 feet to get to the highest leaves of the tallest trees. This seems to contradict a basic law of physics. To raise water that high requires a pressure of about 420 pounds per square inch. However, atmospheric pressure at sea level is only about 15 pounds to the square inch, and this limits the height that a suction pump can raise water to a mere 33 feet. Not only does the tree attain the tremendous pressure required, but it does so with a speed of flow so great that in certain trees water rises at the speed of almost 150 feet an hour.

There have been many explanations of how the tree manages to do this. Until recently, it was often explained that water rose in the same way that blotting paper absorbs water, by capillary action. Capillarity, however, has been shown to account for a rise of only a few feet. Another theory had it that living tissue in the xylem in some way forced the water up. But a botanist disproved this in a monumental experiment. He chopped down a 70-foot oak, immersed it in a vat of acid to kill the living cells, then dipped the trunk in water—which nevertheless continued to move to the top of the tree.

The explanation would seem to lie in the nature of water itself. Water molecules tend to stick together; they have what scientists call great cohesiveness. If, under certain conditions, water is enclosed in a thin tube, it remains as a solid column, resisting even the immense pull of 5,000 pounds per square inch. Plant sap is not quite so cohesive, yet it has a tensile strength which could—in theory—pull a column of sap as a continuous

The complex chemistry of photosynthesis goes on exclusively in the minute confines of the chloroplast like the one shown in the diagram below. Millions of chloroplasts are found in the cells of a single leaf (see pages 102-103) and within each chloroplast there are hundreds of layers of chlorophyll (shown in green below).

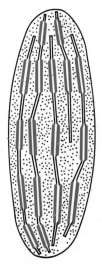

Photosynthesis proceeds in the chloroplast in a series of steps:

● Water molecules brought into the chloroplast from the plant's roots constantly come in contact with the layers of chlorophyll.

● Sunlight passing into the leaf strikes the chlorophyll, giving it the energy to break the water molecules apart.

● The oxygen from the broken water molecule is exhaled by the leaf and the hydrogen stays in the chloroplast —combined with a "driver molecule" that has absorbed the excess energy.

● The energy-laden driver molecule next causes the hydrogen to combine with simple carbon compounds already built up in the chloroplast by carbon dioxide taken from the air.

● With this last reaction, the change from light energy to chemical energy is complete—the complex, stable, energy-rich carbohydrate known as sugar has been formed.

stream to the top of a tree 6,500 feet high. But what force pulls the sap up? Partly it is the upward pressure exerted by the water absorbed by the roots—but mostly the answer lies in pull from the top by the leaves. As droplets of water in the leaves' cells evaporate or are used in photosynthesis, a water deficit is created which causes the entire column of water to rise. This pull, felt in the farthest root, causes a deficit of water in the root hair itself and water is drawn from the soil into the root hair which replaces the droplets lost by the leaf.

Everyone knows that a plant, if kept on a window sill, will turn its leaves toward the light. The plant does not seek out the light. What happens is that the light reduces the concentration of a growth hormone, auxin, on the bright side of the stem. As a result, the dark side grows more rapidly, bending the stem toward the light. Similarly, a gnarled old oak, though it may bear 700,000 leaves, manages to keep them all out of each other's way so that there is a minimum of shading of one leaf by another. This mosaic pattern of leaves is brought about by the bending of the stems to bring the upper surfaces of the leaves to face the strongest light. In addition, the stalks of nearby leaves often grow in different directions and are of different lengths. What appears to be uncanny intelligence in the leaves is actually caused by auxin. When a leaf stalk is shaded, the amount of auxin increases and growth occurs, pushing and bending the leaf until it is in the light, which then reduces the auxin and halts growth.

Most stems grow toward light, but roots tend to grow away from it. Pick up a freshly germinated acorn from the forest floor and examine it. A blanched shoot (the future trunk) will be seen pointing up, and another (the future root) pointing down. Now lay the acorn on its side. Soon the stem will point upward again and the root downward. The reason— auxin. When the stem is lying horizontally, the auxin becomes more concentrated on the side closer to the ground; it makes that side of the stem grow more rapidly, raising the shoot into the air until all sides are receiving equal amounts of light. In the case of the root, auxin works in reverse and acts as an inhibitor of growth. It collects on the bottom side of a root lying on the ground, just as it does in a stem, but this time the *top* side of the root grows faster until the root is headed downward. Thus, no matter how a seed or acorn lands on the forest floor, its primary root will always grow downward and its shoot upward.

Although growth substances have been found to govern much of the life of the tree, roots do not have any mechanism known to scientists that enables them to grow toward water. The reason that roots are often found growing thickly around a drainpipe while roots from the same tree may be sparse under a dry lawn is simply that moisture from the drainpipe encourages the growth of the roots that have already found the moist spot.

Charles Darwin, marveling at the powers of a root tip, once wrote: "It is hardly an exaggeration to say that the tip . . . thus endowed and having the power of directing the movements of adjoining parts acts like the brain of one of the lower animals." Of course plants are insentient. They feel nothing and know nothing, and yet they do extraordinary things. Most extraordinary of all, perhaps, is that their remarkable powers have arisen by blind evolutionary chance, and their responses are the result not of thought but of complex chemical controls.

How Trees Work

TRANSLUCENT CUPS OF YEW BERRIES CONTAIN THE TREE'S SEEDS, WHICH ARE SCATTERED BY BIRDS THAT EAT THE PULPY FRUIT

The way trees work in order to live, grow and reproduce themselves is an almost magical process. Leaves breathe for the tree and manufacture all its food. Roots gather water and minerals. The trunk holds the leaves up to the sunlight, sends them water from the roots, and gets food back from them. Seeds are borne in flowers and cones in a variety of shapes and forms.

LEAF STRUCTURE is shown in the magnified view (*opposite*) of a sugar-maple leaf, and in the conventional view of the leaf (*below*) with a caterpillar eating the soft parts between the veins. Both views show seasonal color variations.

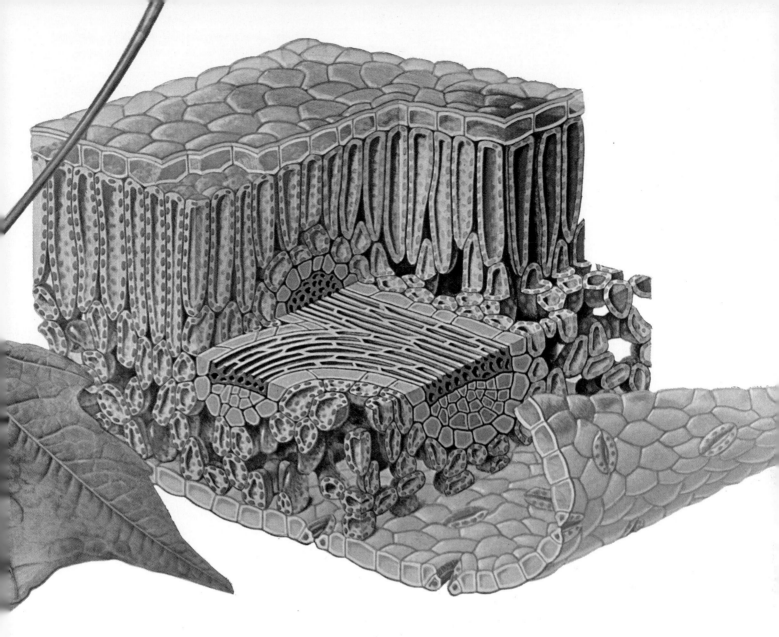

The Workings of a Leaf

How a leaf is designed to carry on the miraculous process of photosynthesis is shown in the drawings of a sugar-maple leaf on these pages. Strong but delicate veins (shown in gray above) hold the leaf out to catch the maximum of sunlight, and also serve as a plumbing system carrying water to the leaf and food to the rest of the tree. The skin of the leaf has a waxy coat to prevent evaporation of water, and is transparent to admit light to the interior of the leaf. Under this skin lie the two main photosynthetic tissues. Both are made up of cells crowded with tiny green bodies called chloroplasts which contain the chlorophyll. The uppermost layer has its cells crowded on end, exposing the most possible chloroplasts to the sun. Beneath this so-called palisade layer are loosely packed cells forming a spongy layer. Air containing the carbon dioxide for photosynthesis comes into the leaf through tiny openings in the bottom skin and moves through the large air spaces in the spongy layer into smaller ones which extend up into the palisade tissue. These pores, called stomata, open and close according to the water pressure in the two sausage-shaped guard cells which flank the opening.

In the fall, the chlorophyll in the leaf disintegrates and a yellow pigment, which was present in the chloroplast all summer, is unmasked. A red pigment dissolved in the liquid part of the cells is also formed in the cool bright days of autumn when sugars accumulate in the dying leaf.

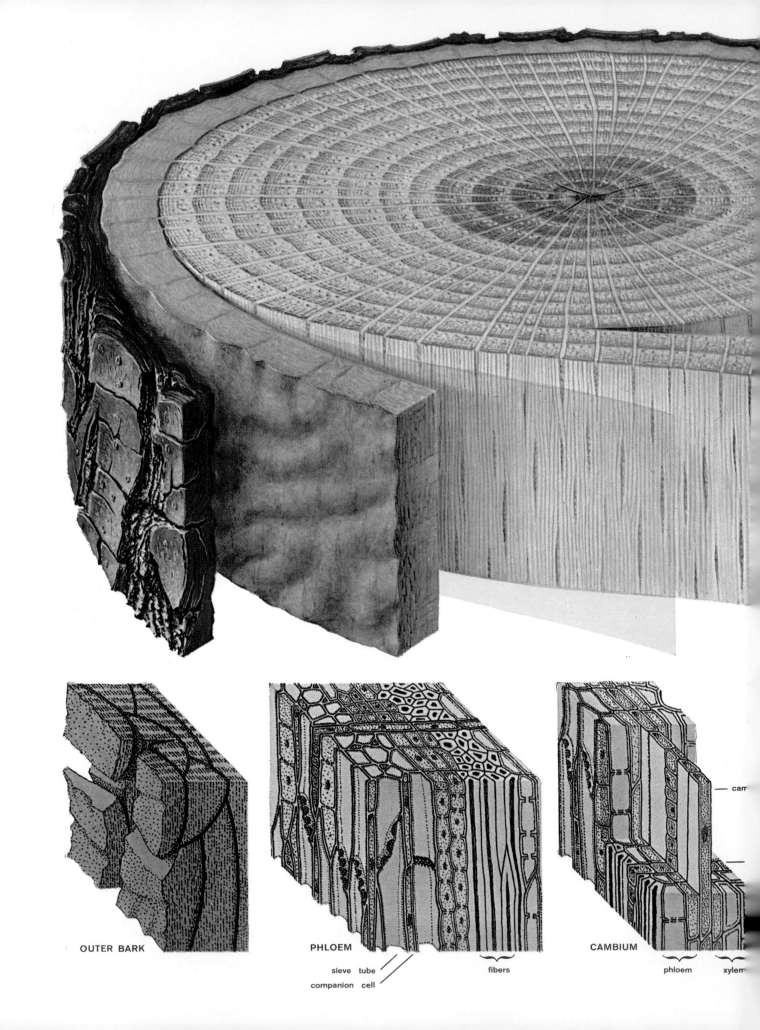

OUTER BARK

PHLOEM

sieve tube

companion cell

fibers

CAMBIUM

phloem

xylem

cam

How a Tree Trunk Grows

For all its size and vitality, for all its impressive thickening from year to year, most of the tissue of a tree trunk does not and *cannot* grow, once it has been formed. The tissue that adds to a tree's size is confined to a microscopically thin layer, the cambium (colored yellow-green in the drawing). As the cambium cells divide, the tree grows in diameter. The new cells formed toward the inside of the tree become wood, or xylem, and the cells on the outside become a layer called phloem. Cells produced in the spring growing season are usually much larger than those produced in the summer. The small size and density of summer cells make them look dark. It is the alternation of the dark summer wood with the lighter-colored spring wood of the following year which produces the rings in trees. In a climate like that throughout most of the United States, a typical hardwood tree will add one ring a year. The tree in this drawing has 12 annual rings and is thus 12 years old. Although its xylem is "dead" in the sense that it cannot divide to form new cells, it nevertheless performs several basic functions in the tree. Its tracheids and vessels pipe water to the leaves and through tiny holes or pits to adjacent cells. In addition, the xylem stores food and forms the support for the tree. With age, the inner part of the xylem ceases to function as a conductive tissue, becoming dark in color as its cells are clogged with gums and other substances. This dark center of the tree is called heartwood, the younger outer xylem is called sapwood. The rays radiating like spokes from the center of the trunk distribute liquids laterally.

The phloem's main function, for a few years after it is formed, is to carry food up and down the tree in its sieve tubes. It also may store food in the form of starches in its companion cells. As it is cut off from the water and food materials inside the tree, it begins to die and then helps to build up the protective outer bark of the tree.

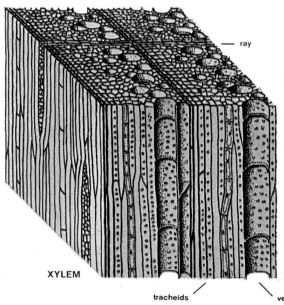

XYLEM

tracheids   vessel

ray

BUTTERNUT

FLOWERING DOGWOOD

SUGAR MAPLE

RED CEDAR

BLUE SPRUCE

AUSTRIAN PINE

AMERICAN ELM

POPLAR

SILVER MAPLE

FLOWERS AND CONES fulfill a similar function for trees. Both make it possible for "male" pollen to be produced and then transported to fertilize "female" ovules. Trees with cones (*center row*) depend on the wind to distribute their pollen. Other trees (*top and bottom*) do this too, but they also have flowers to attract insects, which effect the pollination.

AN ASH BUD exhibits a set of wings that give it the look of a pert young deer. When the buds open in spring, this releases pollen of male trees to fertilize the ovules within the buds of female trees, which are opening at the same time. Willow and poplar are among other common species that separate the sexes into individual male or female trees.

STILT ROOTS of a pandanus, or screw pine, curve gracefully, propping the top-heavy tree to give it resilience in storms. It grows well in either arid or wet soil in tropical climates.

BUTTRESS ROOTS of a strangler fig enclose a host tree. The fig got its start on a branch of the host, sent down roots which grew mightily and will soon choke the host to death.

A BANYAN ON THE ISLAND OF REUNION HAS SEVERAL HUNDRED

Varied Roles for Root Systems in the

Roots serve the double function of anchoring a plant and supplying it with nutrients. They do this in a bewildering variety of ways; they do it in the water, or even high in the air, where no self-respecting root should be. There are roots that breathe, roots that grapple, roots that dangle (*opposite page*), roots that strangle (*bottom left*). One tree, the banyan (*above*), can be said to consist largely of roots. It starts life as a small, totally untreelike plant high in the limbs of a host tree. From here it drops a network of

ANCHORING ROOTS of an aerial plant seem to prefer horizontal limbs and forks of trees, where bits of soil accumulate. At times, however, they even thrive on telephone poles.

BREATHING ROOTS, "knees" of the bald cypress, grow up out of the ground in poorly aerated soil, seeking more oxygen. These knees sometimes grow to a height of three feet.

DESCENDING ROOTS WHICH RESEMBLE A GROVE OF TREES

Survival Struggle

roots to the ground which take hold and ramify in the soil. These grow thicker and stronger until each is like a tree trunk itself. The host ultimately strangles and the banyan remains, a virtual grove consisting of a single interconnected tree. The pandanus, on the other hand, sends out a cluster of stilt roots which help support it in mushy soil when it is young. These work so well that as the pandanus reaches maturity, the base of the tree's central trunk often atrophies without appreciable weakening of its strength.

AERIAL ROOTS of an aroid, known to grow 60 feet long, dangle from the plant's host tree to the river below, ending in webbed rootlets for more efficiency in sucking up water.

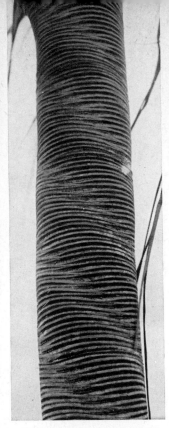

FLUTED STEM OF "MAPE" TREE   STRANGLER FIG AND HOST   BULBOUS ACROCOMIA PALM   LEAF-SCARRED PANDANUS

Columns for the Roof of the Rain Forest

A primary function of tree trunks is to get leaves up in the air, where they can catch sunlight for photosynthesis. Yet, while tree trunks are performing this main function, they take on wildly varying appearances and assume many secondary duties. A slender fluting, possibly having some strengthening effect, is quite common among tropical trees including the "mape" tree of Polynesia. The gnarled "trunk" of the strangler fig is a mass of aerial roots, smothering its host to death. The bulbous part of the Acrocomia stem is a main reservoir of food for the tree. Many

STUNTED AND TWISTED by incessant gales, a species of beech hugs the earth in Tierra del Fuego at South America's tip. In a better environment, it would grow upright.

FINDING SUPPORT, a cabbage palmetto in Florida rises against the trunk of another tree. Uprooted when young, it grew along the ground until it could find a support.

ARECA, A BETEL-NUT PALM   BRAZILIAN WAX PALM   AMAZONIAN PALM   SPINY KAPOK TRUNK

tropical trees bear their leaves directly on their main trunks. The Hawaiian pandanus above has spiral scars where the old leaves have fallen off. Other leaves make rings like those interrupting the smooth shaft of the areca palm. The fruits of this palm, called betel nuts, are chewed by many people throughout tropical Asia. The Brazilian wax palm has a trunk studded with the thornlike bases of old leaves.

While the strange appearances of the trunks above are inherited, trunks are also distorted by environmental factors, as illustrated below.

SQUAT AND MASSIVE, a cultivated kapok grows enormous branches under ideal conditions. In the rain forest, competing for sunlight, it would grow tall and slender.

LOPSIDED AND FLAT-CROWNED, an acacia in French Somaliland bends to the sweep of dry monsoon winds. Grazing goat herds keep the lower branches stripped bare.

111

6

The Web of Forest Life

THE organization of a forest is much like that of a large city, as an examination of the Great Smoky Mountains forest of Tennessee and North Carolina clearly illustrates. It is the largest remaining virgin forest in the East. In it flourish upward of 100 kinds of trees, more than are native to all Europe. The skyscrapers of this forest city are its dominant trees, some of which reach 100 to 150 feet above the ground—tulip trees, basswood, sugar maple, buckeye, hemlock and yellow birch. Beneath these giants, the skyline is filled in by an understory of smaller trees, equivalent to a city's larger apartment buildings—magnolia, holly and others. Nearer the ground are the small apartment buildings—a layer made up of rhododendron, hydrangea and viburnum that send puffs of bloom through the forest alleys. The private homes and shops can be compared to the approximately 100 kinds of herbs that cling to the forest floor. This lowest layer is a miniature city in itself, with a canopy of spreading herbs and ferns and an undergrowth of smaller plants.

The Great Smoky Mountains forest is organized into eight layers—the soil basement, the forest floor, low herbs, high herbs, shrubs, low trees, tall trees and the air above the forest canopy. The organization of tropical rain forests is infinitely more complex; in some the vegetation is arranged in as many as 27 groupings.

Trees are the pillars upon which much of the other forest life is draped. That they create unique conditions for life can be seen clearly if one walks the few yards from a field into a farm wood lot. One's feet almost immediately give notice that a boundary between two worlds has been traversed—the soil in the field is dry and unyielding, the forest floor is moist and springy. It is much darker in the woods; as little as one per cent of the sunlight filters through the various layers to the ground, the rest being reflected or absorbed by the leaves. Whereas it may be hot and windy in the field, a summer forest is cool and the wind is reduced to a gentle breeze, perhaps only a tenth of the velocity outside the forest. If the border between these two worlds is crossed during a shower, the transition is marked in still another way. Much of the rain is intercepted by the canopy. Only when the leaves have been thoroughly wetted does water begin to drip gently to the forest floor. Half of it may never reach the ground at all.

All life in a forest is intimately connected with other life in a chain of relationships which starts with the sun. The forest exists because of energy from the sun. Only green plants can convert sun power into sugar power and thus originate the cycle of food that flows through every living thing in the forest. This stored energy is converted into meat by the animals that eat the plants—by insects that leave no parts of trunks or leaves or roots untouched, by deer that browse on twigs and tender buds, by chipmunks that fill their mouth pouches with seeds and nuts.

The energy originally in the green plant is now available secondhand to another set of forest dwellers which eat the plant eaters. There are many animals—snakes, lizards, predatory insects, many kinds of birds—that do just that. These primary predators in turn are a food supply for secondary predators—shrews, owls, hawks, foxes. And in the end these secondary predators also die and complete the cycle by returning their substance to the soil after death, releasing nutrients that green plants can absorb through their roots and again put into circulation through the forest.

Normally this web of interdependence has a great deal of stretch before it snaps. One member of the forest community may increase rapidly and thus present a threat to the forest, but its pull is usually absorbed by the predators that form other strands. Sometimes, however, a strand snaps entirely and when it does the whole forest web may unravel. That happened about 20 years ago in a magnificent Engelmann spruce forest that had created a whole community of life in the wind-swept high Rocky Mountains of Colorado.

In this community lived a small bark beetle, about the size of a housefly. It preyed upon the aged spruces, hastening their death and making space for the renewal of young growth. These beetles were kept in check for many years by woodpeckers and insect predators, and thus did not exist in sufficient numbers to attack healthy, vigorous trees with any success. Whenever the beetle population began to build up, so did that of the woodpeckers—and the former equilibrium was restored.

DIFFERENT BIRDS live at different levels in the forest, depending on their nesting and feeding habits. Blackburnian warblers prefer hemlock tops; redstarts, sugar maples; magnolia warblers, lower hemlock branches; chestnut-sided warblers, low bushes; ovenbirds, the cover of the forest floor.

Then a severe windstorm ripped through this Colorado forest, leveling many of the shallow-rooted spruces. The beetles found an abundant food supply secure from the woodpeckers, which could not reach them in the tangle of branches formed by the wind-thrown trees. Within three years the beetles had increased astronomically in number. So great was their population that even the vigorous trees could not withstand the onslaught. Hordes of beetles laid their eggs in galleries under the bark, and there the young fed, girdling the trees and dooming them. The beetles hastened the process by carrying a fungus disease with them. In a period of only six years after the outbreak began, enough timber had been destroyed to build houses for nearly two million people—16 times more timber than had been consumed in the same area by fires in all the previous 30 years.

Because of the snapping of a single thread, a mighty forest was doomed. The whole superstructure of life erected upon the spruce perished with it—the woodpeckers and the other forest dwellers that had now lost their food and shelter, the soil inhabitants that had once found a favorable environment under the cool moist layer of needles. Man ultimately felt the effects of the unraveling of the web, for he too is affected by the fate of a forest. The water that formerly sank into the sponge of forest soil now ran unobstructed down the mountain, adding to flood hazards.

EVEN a superficial examination of forest creatures will reveal that they are specialized for life there. Some of the specializations are remarkably ingenious. Most owls, which hunt at night—because that is when the rodents they eat are abroad—have very large eyes packed with light-sensitive cells. This enables them to capture darting mice without hitting tree branches in light no stronger than that produced by a candle burning at a distance of 1,170 feet. Owls are also aided by remarkably acute hearing —in part due to their unusually large eardrums and ear openings, but also to the fact that in many owls one ear opening is larger than the other. These adaptations give the birds a different sound pattern at each ear and enable them to locate noise sources very precisely.

The mesh of branches in the forest makes rapid movement difficult for many animals, especially large ones. Africa is full of big animals but only a handful, such as the elephant, buffalo, okapi, wild hog and leopard, live in the rain forest. Each possesses one or more adaptations for moving through the undergrowth—strength and weight of body, short limbs, a wedge-shaped head. Birds sometimes suffer accidents in threading their way through the forest but the Accipiter hawks, commonly known as darters, speed through the tangle like phantoms, pouncing on small birds. The goshawk, sharp-shinned and Cooper's hawks are all slim-bodied with short wings and tails like rudders. The Cooper's hawk's tail, for example, is nearly as long as its whole body and it opens and closes, twists and turns like a living fan. In addition, its wings have short secondary feathers which correspond to an airplane's flaps and increase efficiency.

Many forest animals have taken to the trees and have developed adaptations for an existence there. Members of the tree frog family, common in forests around the world, have large rounded discs on the ends of their toes. A sticky glandular secretion helps make these pads adhesive. In addition they are fashioned like friction grips with small projections on their surfaces. Tree frogs are thus able to climb a smooth-barked tree, or even a windowpane, with ease. Adhesive discs have also developed on the feet of forest-inhabiting lizards, bats, porcupines—and some African gecko lizards even have adhesive ridges on their tails.

Perhaps the most remarkable of the tree-dwelling mammals are those that have developed parachutes. The North American flying squirrel possesses flaps of skin between its front and hind legs. This nearly doubles the under-surface area of its body without significantly increasing its weight, and permits it to make long gliding flights from tree to tree. During these the animal exerts considerable control over its flight by the slant of its tail or a change in the tension of the flaps. Just before it reaches its landing place, the squirrel flips its tail upward, thus slanting its body up so it can grasp the trunk with all four feet, and also slowing its landing speed. It then scampers up the tree to launch itself on another glide. Some gliding mammals achieve phenomenal distances: an Australian species of flying phalanger, the greater glider, can glide for 360 feet, and one was even observed to cover 1,770 feet in six successive flights.

THE SUGAR GLIDER is a marsupial, found in Australia, which resembles the flying squirrels of the northern forests. Active only at night, it catapults itself from treetops, sailing long distances to flee peril.

WOODPECKERS are perfectly fitted for their role of climbing on tree trunks and extracting insects hidden under the bark. Their claws are sharp and curved, and many species have two toes permanently turned backward, instead of only one as with most birds, giving them a strong grip on a branch. The woodpecker's tail has unusually stiff and strong feathers and is used as a third leg to provide an additional prop against the bark.

A woodpecker is an animated chisel. It digs into wood by knocking out small chips with its bill. It grasps the tree with its claws, props itself with its stiff tail, then bends back the upper part of its body to put force behind each swing. It can beat its head against wood 20 times a second, in uninterrupted bursts of almost an hour, and dig holes more than a foot deep into the heartwood of a living tree. In the process, it sets up vibrations in its skull that would probably kill any other bird. But a woodpecker's head is unusually thick, so heavy in fact that a young bird cannot hold it up. The skull is jar-proof because the bones between the beak and the cranium are connected by spongy tissue which absorbs the vibrations before they reach the brain. The tongue, too, displays remarkable adaptations—sticky, pointed and often with barbs at the tip, an efficient instrument for harpooning wood borers out of small tunnels in the wood and from under bark. The tongue is enormously long, in some woodpeckers about five times the length of the beak itself, and is kept curled inside the mouth.

This wealth of forest life could not all find living space were not certain adjustments made to utilize the forest for maximum occupancy. Forests are the homes of multitudes of insect species, yet they offer comparatively little competition to each other. Some seek nectar from flowers, others feed on the green leaves or bore galleries in the wood. Some suck sap from leaves, branches and roots. Twenty different insect species feed on the white pine in North America. Five of the species attack the pine's foliage, three its buds, three bore into twigs, two are wood borers which attack the trunk and larger branches and two others are root borers, one feeds on bark and four consume the growing tissue in the cambium layer.

Insects are often specialized not only as to the kinds of leaves they consume, but also the particular portions: some insects have jaws adapted for cutting leaves, others for piercing leaves to suck the plant juices. Among the most interesting of the leaf insects are the minute larvae of certain beetles, flies, wasps and moths. Known as leaf miners, they feed between the two epidermal layers of a leaf. They are usually flat in shape, their legs absent or severely reduced in size; some kinds have a wedge-shaped head, an efficient tool for separating the two epidermal layers as they progress through the leaf. The paths of miners can be traced as wavy lines, squares or intricate filigrees, each species making its own pattern. "They write their signatures in the leaves," says one entomologist.

Examine the branch of an oak in late summer and almost inevitably one will see hanging from it a structure that somewhat resembles a small brown apple. If the oak apple is plucked from the tree and kept under an inverted tumbler, small wasps will eventually appear inside the glass, having tunneled through minute exit holes made in the walls of the apple. These oak apples are nurseries of small insects and are known as galls. There are about 2,000 kinds of gall insects in the United States that attack roots, trunk and leaves. The gall made by each is constant in form, color, texture and internal structure. Although caused by insects (and also sometimes by fungi, mites and nematodes), they are grown by the tree itself and are much more conspicuous than the tiny creatures that cause them. Very few galls seriously affect the vigor of the tree, and in most cases they are no more than nonmalignant tumors that will be gotten rid of when the tree sheds its leaves.

OAK GALLS are harmless tumors produced on oak leaves when an irritating fluid is injected into them by insects. The insect larvae live inside the gall and emerge as adults through holes which they bore.

What is so intriguing about galls is that they are growths induced by agents external to the plant. By merely injecting the plant with a chemical substance that acts as an irritant, an insect is able to provoke the oak to grow what is in effect a new organ—one specifically adapted to nurture and shelter the young insects. Equally remarkable are some of the things the oak does which ensure that the gall will not be eaten or damaged by other creatures. Unpalatable substances may be formed in the tissue of the gall; often the surface of the gall develops hairs and spines; again, its wall may thicken and harden or become modified in shape to resemble a flower, fruit, seed or fungus.

The abundance of insects constitutes a prime source of food for birds, which also populate the forest in large numbers. They, too, live with a minimum of competition among species because of their precise adaptation to the multitude of niches the forest city offers. Certain species nest and feed primarily in evergreen forests, others in forests of deciduous trees. In part, this preference is due to a difference in the floor in each kind of forest: the deciduous floor usually consists of rich, loose humus with an abundance of creatures, whereas the needle leaves of an evergreen forest accumulate to form a thick layer that decomposes slowly and contains fewer insects and other small animals.

Other factors are more subtle. One ornithologist believes that choice is determined primarily by differences in the size and shape of leaves. For example, the red-eyed vireo builds its nest almost exclusively in deciduous trees; perhaps one reason is that this bird habitually feeds near the tips of small twigs or from the broadleaf surfaces themselves. This habit pattern is poorly fitted to feeding on hemlock, not only because of the arrangement of the needles but because the needles furnish less surface area from which insects can be gleaned. Parula warblers in the southern United States nest in the hanging draperies of Spanish moss that festoon many of the trees. In the north, where there is no Spanish moss, the nest is usually built in a tuft of usnea lichen which closely resembles Spanish moss and is commonly called old-man's-beard moss. Where there is no moss, this warbler is extremely rare.

In addition to seeking out certain kinds of vegetation within a forest, bird species tend to arrange themselves in layers. The ruffed grouse, ovenbird, hermit thrush and junco are rarely found nesting anywhere but on the forest floor; orioles, crows, hawks and eagles almost always nest on the topmost branches in the forest. A study made some years ago in a New York State forest dominated by sugar maples, hemlocks and beeches revealed that the warblers populated well-defined nesting niches according to species, thus reducing competition and enabling a large variety of warblers to occupy the same forest. For example, the Blackburnian warbler inhabited the tops of evergreens, the black-throated green chose the middle branches and the magnolia the lowest. Other warblers selected shaded shrubs and still others sunlit shrubs.

MAN, too, is a member of the forest community—probably its most destructive one. Everywhere woods have sounded to the ringing of his ax and the crackle of his fires, until he has reduced much of the world's virgin forest to a jumble of thickets and impoverished earth. Until a century ago, the tropical rain forest remained relatively unscathed, but now it too is being demolished to make way for plantations of bananas, rubber and cocoa. Even the pulse of native life, which once beat in time to the green heart of the tropics, is becoming altered as one primitive society after another accelerates the white man's demolition by clearing wide areas of rain forest to eke out scanty crops on infertile soil.

But there are still small segments of humankind that live in the forest. The purest example is perhaps the African Pygmy, who inhabits the primeval Ituri jungle of northeastern Congo. "Children of the Forest," the Pygmies call themselves, an appropriate name since they are better adapted physically than other humans to forest life. With their low weight (average male, 88 pounds) and lithe bodies they can clamber up trees with astonishing agility, or make their way smoothly and swiftly through the dense forest growth. In the warm, humid climate, their small size combined with slenderness enables them to dissipate body heat quickly.

The Pygmies depend on their mother forest for all the essentials of life. It is a haven of safety into which they can melt like animals. They construct their shelters from saplings and cover them with large leaves. Their loincloths are made from sheets of bark, pounded with an elephant-tusk mallet. They have no need to store food or raise crops, for a sufficiency of fruits, nuts and game is never far away. The Pygmies are aware of the debt they owe the forest and they attribute to it all good that flows to their little bands. When misfortune occurs, they feel that the forest has gone to sleep. So they sing and talk to it, calling it "mother" or "friend," knowing that if it is wakeful it will attend to their needs.

The world of the Pygmy is disappearing before the onslaught of civilization, yet they continue to cling to a way of life that is conducted with dignity, gentleness and in complete harmony with their environment— an existence which other human societies have largely forsaken.

BUILDING A HUT, A WOMAN OF THE AFRICAN PYGMY TRIBE OF BAMBUTIS ADDS A FINISHING TOUCH OF LEAVES AROUND THE DOOR

Man in the Forest

At the apex of the forest community are human beings who live in it—Pygmies in Africa, Indians in South America, Negritos in Asia. While they are primitive, they show intelligence in adapting themselves to their environment and they have an elaborate social organization. Forest peoples probably have the innate ability for more complex life, but they prefer the woods.

IN A PYGMY CAMP BaMbutis take their ease after a day's hunting. Since they raise no animals for food, the BaMbutis, using bows and poison-tipped arrows, must capture their meat in the surrounding forest. At left and right are huts that house family groups. The beehive-shaped frames are made from bent saplings and thatched with broad leaves.

"Children of the Forest"

The BaMbuti Pygmies are amiable people who seldom grow taller than four feet eight inches. They live in the Ituri rain forest in the Congo and call themselves "Children of the Forest." The forest is indeed their parent. When the BaMbutis are at leisure (*left*), it offers their young such toys as whistles made from fruits and tops made from nuts. It inspires the adults to dance and to sing songs whose theme is "the forest is good, the forest is kind."

The forest provides well for the daily needs of the BaMbutis, who are nomadic. When they pitch their camps, the men go out to hunt and the women gather mushrooms, nuts, edible roots and fruits. After about a month, when the game has been frightened away and the nearby vegetables exhausted, the BaMbutis move on.

The BaMbutis engage in trade and social intercourse with neighboring Negroes. They have acquired Negro habits like smoking (*below*). But they retain their identity as forest dwellers and will not integrate into the outer world. They insist, "When the forest dies, its children die."

SMOKING PYGMY puffs on a banana-stem pipe (*right*). The pipestem and the tobacco are obtained from nonforest Negroes. The uncured leaf quickly brings on mild dizziness.

STRETCHING A NET, a hunter prepares to catch game. Nets made from vines are 100 to 300 feet long and four feet high. Each married man in a hunting group owns one.

SEIZING A CATCH (*left*), the hunter picks up a small antelope from his net. As many as 25 families will fan out and beat the bushes to frighten animals into the long net traps.

OUT HUNTING (*opposite*), a Pygmy party carries bows, arrows and nets. The arrows are poisoned with strophanthin, which can kill a small animal with a mere scratch.

A GUAICA BRAVE, member of a South American Indian tribe, exhibits a ceremonial dyeing of the head and shoulders with madder. The arm band is made of monkey fur.

The Guaica Indians

In the forests around the headwaters of the Orinoco River in South America live the Guaica Indians, who are somewhat more advanced than the African Pygmies. They are not congenitally stunted. Their culture centers on a primitive agriculture rather than on a nomadic existence. But they are still a forest people. The Guaicas know how to transplant bananas, which are one of their major staples. They roast and boil peach-palm fruit. They grow cotton for their scanty clothing and tobacco for pleasure. Since missionaries reached them in the last decade, the Guaicas have taken up the cultivation of yams and sweet potatoes.

Their aptitudes for survival and progress have made the Guaicas one of the few primitive peoples that currently show a population growth. They are also slowly but surely expanding the territory that they inhabit. They still lack the ability to build canoes or to make metal tools. But acquiring such skills could be a mixed blessing. Exposure to more complex civilizations often does damage to primitive peoples by destroying cultural patterns developed through thousands of years which make life in the forest possible.

THE GUAICA HABITAT is like this submontane rain forest in the Amazon River basin. The perpetually green expanse is very hot and the rainfall in places exceeds 100 inches a year.

Part of the rain forest is almost impassable jungle, where the tall trees are aswarm with orchids and are festooned with lianas. But there are also open woods and savannas.

It is in the forest that Indians like the Guaicas live after having been driven there many years ago by people who were more skilled in the arts of warfare and civilization.

125

A Life of Hunting and Primitive Farming

Although Guaicas have an aggressive reputation, they enjoy a well-ordered community life, broken down into small family groups. The women are responsible for the maintenance of the settlement and gather the fruit of the wild peach palm.

They also weave baskets and make their own simple ornaments. Unlike Pygmies, who must carry fire with them, the Guaicas know how to make it by friction. The men go hunting with long bows made of palm wood and wood-tipped

arrows fashioned from tough arrow grass. Guaica men are more brightly adorned than the women. They paint themselves with a kind of madder in patterns supposed to bring good luck while on the hunt. Both sexes affect a monklike tonsure.

A WORKING MOTHER carries her baby in a sling as she brings home a basket of peach-palm fruit on her back. She has additional fruit in baskets decorated with a snake motif.

GUAICA HOME (*left*) is a lean-to characteristically built against the buttress of a large tree. The long bows and arrows always come in sets of three—one bow, two arrows.

MALES ON PARADE strut in a settlement (*below*). The skin markings like jaguar paw prints indicate that they have reached manhood, and also serve to camouflage them.

127

Subhuman Forest Dwellers

The great apes, mankind's closest relatives, are all forest dwellers. African gorillas (*below*) live on the ground or in low trees and are clumsy climbers. Their troops have leaders, who are obeyed and affectionately trusted. The East Indian orangutan, whose name in Malay means "wild man," is awkward on the ground and agile in trees. It is less gregarious than gorillas are.

A GROUP OF GORILLAS headed by a large female (*above, right*) wanders through a rain forest in the Congo. Contrary to popular belief, gorillas are actually shy and amiable.

A HUNGRY ORANGUTAN in Borneo (*opposite*) clasps a foul-smelling but delicious durian fruit. It sleeps in a nest 25 to 40 feet above ground, building a fresh one every night.

BRACKET FUNGUS forms tell-
tale shelves on a feeble oak.
Fungi attack ailing trees, rid-
dling their tissues with fibers
that eventually penetrate deep
into the heartwood and rot it.

7

The
Hidden World
of the Soil

THE dead leaves, needles, twigs and fallen branches that lie in heaps upon
the forest floor appear at a casual glance to be a lifeless, rotting mass.
Actually, they form the roof tops of the hidden world of the forest soil. The
soil veneer shelters more life than can be found in any other stratum of the
forest, or probably any other environment on earth, for that matter. The inhabitants exist in numbers that stagger the imagination. They carpet the
grains of soil and weave passageways through them; they dig out burrows
and tunnels and underground nests. The honeycombs of moles, the burrows
of worms often form such a labyrinth in the forest floor that it has the springy
feel of foam rubber. Some years ago, scientists blocked off a small section of
forest soil in New York State and removed the top layer of earth to a depth
of one inch. They made a careful count of the insects and other invertebrates
found among the soil crumbs. In all, there was an average of 1,356 living
creatures present in each square foot, including 865 mites, 265 springtails,
22 millepedes, 19 adult beetles and various numbers of 12 other forms. Had

an estimate also been made of the microscopic population, it might have ranged up to two billion bacteria and many millions of fungi, protozoa and algae—in a mere *teaspoonful* of soil.

The forest floor is also a crossroads through which pass aboveground forms that spend part of their lives in the subterranean darkness. About 95 per cent of all the insect species in the world invade the soil in either the egg, larval, pupal or adult stages; the longest-term tenant is a species of cicada which passes 17 years of its nymphal life in the soil and the remaining few weeks of its life as an adult sucking sap from the trees. Many animals spend their resting hours in burrows in the earth. And, of course, plants span both worlds of sunlight and darkness; there is a special place on the plant, called the crown, where the stem and roots meet.

UNDERGROUND is a scene of considerable turmoil, for massive works are being accomplished. Every year, roughly two tons of plant and animal detritus—leaves, twigs, branches, animal droppings, insect corpses —fall like a rain upon an acre of forest floor. Were it not for the work of the soil creatures, the forest would soon be choked in its own wastes. Essential supplies of substances necessary for plant growth would be locked up in these dead remains and renewal of the forest would cease. Air or water could not reach the tree roots through the thick layer of matted leaves and heaps of vegetation.

But the detritus is turned under, plowed and furrowed, broken down into its constituent chemical parts, mixed with the soil grains in a continuing cycle that insures the perpetual rebirth of the forest. In time, everything that lives in the forest returns to the soil, where it is transformed. When alive, the tissues were made up of complex substances—but slowly they are converted again into the simple chemicals from which they were built. Everyone has witnessed a part of this process, commonly known as decay, or rotting, and most people regard it as a spontaneous chemical change. This is not so; decomposition consists of a long and intricate series of steps, not at all clearly understood by scientists, in which a procession of soil creatures with complex interrelationships takes part in attacking the detritus. There is nothing haphazard about the order in which the litter is eaten, mixed and eaten again until it has become what is commonly known as humus.

Only a relatively small number of the soil animals can feed on freshly fallen plant matter before it has been softened and predigested by bacteria and fungi. One that can is the termite, which is able to eat the tissues of deadwood because the protozoa it carries in its stomach digest the wood's tough cellulose. Another is the earthworm, a flexible tube into which go leaves and mineral particles. At its pointed front end, protruding "lips" are pushed out which moisten leaf particles with enzymes so that they are partially predigested before they enter the worm's body. They then pass into the esophagus, where glands secrete a calcium compound serving to neutralize the acids in the leaf tissue. A gizzard grinds up the particles into pieces, which are then further refined in a digestive tract extending through 80 additional segments of the worm's body. What emerges are the worm's castings, tiny mounds which cover the forest floor and which may often be seen on garden paths.

Aristotle regarded earthworms as "the intestines of the earth," but the first person to understand the importance of the earthworm as a soil factor was Gilbert White, the 18th Century British naturalist. He stated with

THE BRISTLETAIL, which feeds on decayed matter, is called primitively wingless because, unlike most insects, it displays no evolutionary evidence of ever having borne wings.

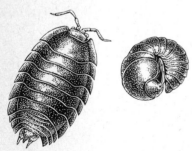

WOOD LICE, also called pill bugs because they curl into a ball when disturbed, are akin to crabs rather than insects. Often found under logs, they feed on rotting wood.

some exaggeration, "Earthworms, though in appearance a small and despicable link in the chain of nature, yet if lost, would make a lamentable chasm. . . . The earth without them would soon become cold, hard-bound, and void of fermentation; and consequently sterile." It was Charles Darwin who actually tried to determine scientifically the earthworm's importance. After lengthy observations and experiments, some of them spanning nearly his whole scientific life, Darwin concluded that on a single acre earthworms each year passed through their bodies enough soil and litter to produce between seven and a half and 18 tons of castings. It is now known that, on some soils at least, Darwin's estimate was highly conservative: one investigator in Africa concluded that 107 tons of castings per acre were deposited during a six-month rainy season. Earthworms rarely eat certain kinds of leaves, such as oak and pine, and are consequently rather scarce where those trees grow. But in areas of favored trees (aspen, ash, hickory, dogwood and basswood), the top several inches of soil may be made up almost entirely of their castings, and there may be millions of worms to an acre.

Most of the other soil animals—such as millepedes, mites, springtails and pill bugs—are unable to digest fresh litter until it has been softened by microorganisms. But then they attack it relentlessly, chewing and grinding it and depositing it as ever-smaller pieces. As the pieces of leaf become smaller and smaller, their combined surface area increases greatly—and thus provides a vast living space for more and more soil microbes. Bacteria feed on these leaf particles, building their energy from the sugars and starches that were originally in the leaves and, in the process, liberating the carbon dioxide that the tree took in through the leaves to carry on photosynthesis. The carbon dioxide is released into the soil and from there it filters back into the atmosphere, where it will someday be re-used by green plants.

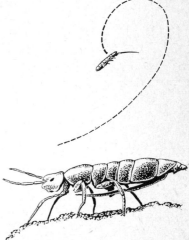

THE SPRINGTAIL, primitively wingless like the bristletail (*opposite*), is able to jump high into the air by using a trigger-like mechanism which extends forward beneath its abdomen.

But the principal agents in the reduction of litter to humus in a forest are the fungi; in many woodland soils, their bulk alone equals the combined weight of all other soil life. They are the scavengers that can decompose almost anything the bacteria do not tackle (and having done so, many of them in turn serve as food for bacteria). They are the chief decomposers, for example, of lignin, one of the main constituents of wood, which is bacteria-resistant. The fungi form many cogs in the machinery of disintegration, starting with the trunks and branches of downed trees. They reduce these hulks of wood to smaller pieces, at which point other kinds of fungi take over, continually softening and reducing the wood to simpler substances. They are vital in the workings of the coniferous forest, for few animals, if any, can attack a newly fallen evergreen needle. However, as soon as a fungus has partially softened a needle, soil invertebrates are able to lay eggs in it and their young continue the process of disintegration.

Much of the humus of forest soil is made by fungi and a goodly amount of the organic matter in the soil consists of their own decaying structures; their ghostlike filaments lace the soil with a fine mesh and often actually bind the soil particles in place. A single ounce of forest soil may contain nearly two miles of fungus strands. A fungus spore, upon germinating, produces a threadlike white strand called a hypha which grows and lengthens, branches and rebranches. Each thread branches into more threads, perhaps every half hour, and each sub-branch may grow at the rate of a hundredth of an inch an hour. In that way, in only a few days under favorable conditions a

THE MILLEPEDE thrives in damp areas and feeds mostly on decaying vegetable matter, though a few species eat growing plants. They can actually have as many as 200 legs each.

fungus may grow miles of strands. The hyphae secrete enzymes and acids that attack the litter, predigest it and break it down into simpler substances that are then absorbed into the fungus. Fungi are among the most economical feeders known; they can retain for building their own structures as much as half of the food they absorb. The absorbed nutrients are immediately put to work to manufacture new cells to attack wood with more enzymes and acids, and so on, endlessly.

To the woodswalker, the most conspicuous evidence of fungi is a short-lived reproductive phase, the toadstool, or mushroom (an edible toadstool). The toadstool, which appears to rise magically out of the litter after a warm rain, starts as a little ball that grows in the direction of the soil surface from the underground bundle of strands. All parts of the toadstool—its umbrella and stalk and spore-shedding mechanism—are mapped out in this little ball, much like a balloon before it is blown up. After a rain, it absorbs water and nutrients and surges through the soil surface. Usually on the underside of the umbrella are gills, or pores, from which clouds of reproductive spores are shed to be carried by wind. They are not shed all at once; instead salvo after salvo of ripened spores bursts into the air. If a fresh toadstool is brought from the woods into a darkened room and a flashlight held under the gills, the spores may be seen raining down like motes in a sunbeam. The number of spores released by some forest toadstools is staggering —some individuals even send out hundreds of millions an hour, and there may be a dozen of these toadstools perched on a single fallen log.

Many forest trees enter into a partnership with soil fungi and appear to gain a major part of their nourishment from the hyphae that either mantle their roots or else penetrate the root cells themselves. Roots of this kind are known as mycorhizae or "fungus roots"—neither roots nor fungi alone, but special structures formed by the combination of the two. The extent of fungus roots is not known for certain, but the partnership is undoubtedly widespread. One authority states that there is no species of woody plant on which fungus roots do not occur. They are particularly common in conifers and orchids, although many kinds of deciduous trees also have them; in recent years it has been learned that they even exist on the roots of some agricultural crops.

What benefit does each member of this strange partnership receive? The trees are undoubtedly able to survive in many places because the fungus partner is an efficient collector of necessary nourishment, which it serves to the tree roots; the tree may also receive from the fungus certain growth-promoting substances. About 90 per cent of the absorbing roots of a conifer are likely to be surrounded by a mantle of fungus, and the fungus roots may be the reason that conifers are able to grow in inhospitable locations. For example, the growth of white-pine seedlings possessing many fungus roots was once experimentally compared with the growth of pines that had very few fungus partners. After a short time the former weighed nearly twice as much, and had absorbed from the soil 86 per cent more nitrogen, 75 per cent more potassium, 234 per cent more phosphorus than the latter. In return, the fungus appears to receive from the tree roots certain elements which may be important for its own growth and reproduction; also, by attaching themselves to the tree roots, some fungi seem to benefit by having staked out a province where they appear to be free from the competition of other fungi,

THE MOLE CRICKET takes its name from the subterranean burrows it digs with shovel-like front legs. It leaves its tunnels only at night, feeding by day upon roots of plants.

bacteria and soil insects. In any event, there has been great controversy among scientists as to whether the fungus is merely a parasite on the tree, whether a full-scale partnership exists that gives mutual benefits or whether the tree and fungus have worked out some sort of uneasy truce.

As in the aboveground world, the hordes of soil life have attracted predators. The myriad strands of fungi are a constant food supply for many small soil dwellers—mites, springtails, beetles and gnats. Through the forest floor swarm animals that feed indiscriminately on each other or on the smaller decay-causing creatures. Centipedes and pseudoscorpions comb the upper layers of the litter, and speedy predaceous beetles prowl through the miniature jungle of the surface. Ants are everywhere. In the tropical forest, the army ants of the New World and the driver ants of Africa send out raiding columns that devour every living thing that cannot fly or flee at great speed. The little shrew is untiring as it races about in its search for insects, worms and rodents. This bundle of energy, sometimes only two or three inches from snout to tail tip, burns tissue with startling rapidity. It carries on its body processes at a speed faster than any other vertebrate animal's, except for the hummingbird. It must eat constantly, at least once an hour, to maintain its breakneck pace of living. It wears itself out in little over a year.

The mole plows the forest soil in its ceaseless search for insects and worms. Its runways are often conspicuous, for when burrowing in the upper layers of soil it lifts ridges that wind across the floor. The mole is marvelously adapted to its life as a bulldozer. Its body is elongated, making it better able to fit through narrow tunnels in the earth. The limbs are short and strong, built not for speed but for moving quantities of earth. Its fur is so arranged that it does not muss even when the animal is moving backwards, and thus offers little resistance to the passage through the soil. Its front paws are in the shape of shovels, equipped with strong claws and so attached that they are twisted outward. The mole's progress through the soil is similar to that of a human swimmer. One arm is brought forward in front of its snout, with the palm facing outward. Then the powerful shoulder muscles snap the arm back, pushing the soil aside and propelling the mole's body forward a few inches. Then the other arm reaches forward. With constant strokes, the mole works its way through the soil, churning perhaps 300 feet of tunnels a day. This teeming life under the blanket of dead leaves creates a hive of passageways that make the soil a sponge retaining vital water supplies.

THE MOLE has strong forelegs and shovel-like claws, ideal for tunneling through the soil in quest of earthworms and insects. It cannot survive more than 12 hours without food.

THE broader architecture of the soil is revealed whenever a road is cut through a forest. Then it can be seen that the soil is built up of a number of different layers, called horizons, that begin at the surface and continue down to bedrock, each kind of soil having its own particular arrangement. There are generally three main horizons (in which soil scientists recognize many subdivisions). The topmost layer consists usually of dark topsoil, a mixture of plant roots and heaps of decaying matter, rich in humus, moist and feeling like bread crumbs in the hand. Beneath this is the subsoil horizon, usually containing small pebbles and stones; it is drier and usually lighter in color and penetrated by fewer roots; it is also gritty to the touch. The lowermost horizon is composed primarily of the splintered chunks of rock that underlie the true soil.

Almost all Temperate Zone soils possess these horizons, but they differ widely, depending on the climate and the kind of underlying rocks from which they were ultimately created. In a trip around the United States the observer may see various kinds of soil along road banks or railroad cuts—the gray soils of the desert sagebrush country of Wyoming, the gray-brown soils of the eastern deciduous forests, the rich brown soils of the Pacific Northwest rain forests. In the tropics, the rain-forest soils will reveal themselves as bright red or orange.

The structure of the soil plays its part in determining the kinds of trees that grow in particular locations in the forest. Generally, the denser the subsoil, the more slowly it absorbs water. If the topsoil layer is thin, the total amount of water absorbed is small, and only trees that grow well under dry conditions can survive. Most tree species are distributed according to the amount of moisture they need, although some, such as black locust, grow well under many soil conditions, deep or shallow, moist or dry.

WHEN peasants examined the soil of the Russian coniferous forest, they noted a deep layer just beneath the surface which was grayish in color and appeared to be composed of ashes left by forest fires. These soils came to be known as "podzol," the Russian word for "ashes." The ashy layer is not the result of fires, but has a much more complicated history. The needles on the floor of evergreen forests decay slowly, largely because of low bacteria populations and the absence of earthworms, and thus form a tight heap of undecayed matter. When this layer is attacked by fungi, a chemical reaction takes place that results in the production of acids, which the rains wash downward, carrying away with them large amounts of the minerals in the subsoil. Thus the topmost soil horizon in a coniferous forest usually consists of a mass of plant materials in various stages of decomposition on the surface, underlain by a sterile layer, acidic and lacking in minerals—the "ashes" —in which few tree roots can grow. These are the true podzol soils that are found throughout the north woods and on wet mountainsides, as well as in many of the pine lands in the southern states.

There are some deciduous forests, composed almost exclusively of oaks, that have a similar soil. The tough, leathery oak leaves cover the ground with a thick layer that is not easily blended with the mineral soil. That is because oak leaves contain a high proportion of tannin, the same material that is used to toughen and preserve leather. This makes them resistant to decay by microbes and apparently unpalatable to earthworms. Thus the leaves accumulate over long periods of time, often stifling the undergrowth almost completely.

Where many other kinds of deciduous trees grow along with oaks, the forest soil can become deep and rich, the decomposed litter mingling with the mineral grains so that there is a gradual transition from the freshly fallen litter on the surface to soil with large amounts of humus beneath. Earthworms are usually credited with creating this type of soil—"mull"—for it is in the mixed deciduous forests that they find their favored kinds of leaves and preferred soil conditions. This type of forest soil when cleared is productive of crops, for it is loose and porous for the entrance of water. It is the home of some of the most attractive woodland flowers—jack-in-the-pulpit, anemone, bloodroot and Dutchman's breeches. Each year it is replenished by the addition of minerals and organic matter from the rain of leaves and branches. They are immediately attacked by the billions of soil organisms—which insures the leafing out of another spring.

ONE OF MANY AGENTS OF FOREST DECAY, A SLIME MOLD SENDS UP ITS FRUITS FROM THE ORGANIC MATTER IN WHICH IT GROWS

Death and Decay

The forces of destruction in the forest are essential to life. Without the work of slime molds, bacteria, mushrooms and other agencies of decay, the stock of chemicals on which life depends would remain locked in dead matter. Instead, the vital materials are liberated to feed fresh growth, which too will die and have its useful elements liberated again by decay.

CHEMICALS ARE SURRENDERED to the soil by the decaying carcass of an elk. Calcium phosphate in the skeleton is dissolved by water and broken down by bacteria into calcium and phosphorus. The phosphorus, which is indispensable to life, is picked up by plants. When animals eat the plants, they use the phosphorus to make bone tissue.

THE GROUND IS PLOWED constantly by earthworms, which are among the most important animals in the world. They literally eat their way through the soil, swallowing it below ground and depositing it on the surface as small piles of rich manure. They also leave behind tunnels, into which air, water, plants, bacteria and various insects penetrate.

SCALE INSECTS suck juice from trees and choke them with scales which they secrete. At left is an oyster-shell scale on an infected poplar, at right a pine-leaf scale.

Insects as Plant Destroyers

Hordes of insects help to keep forest conditions in balance between life and death. They attack and ravage trees, drinking in their sap, chewing their leaves, creating insidious gall growths on them and nibbling their roots. But as the insects destroy, they also start the process of tree decay, out of which eventually comes food for new plants.

Meanwhile, the insect world subtly regulates its capacity to destroy. Some of the harmful aphids are protected by ants because they secrete a "honeydew" that ants gladly eat, but ladybugs keep aphids in check by devouring them.

APHIDS, ONE OF THE MOST NUMEROUS AND DAMAGING GROUPS OF INSECTS, SWARM OVER A STEM. APHIDS KILL LEAVES

ICHNEUMON WASP drills into a branch preparatory to laying eggs on its victim, a sawfly larva living inside. Sawfly larvae promote decay by burrowing in deadwood.

A 17-YEAR LOCUST prepares a slit in a twig to deposit eggs, damaging the twig badly. Nymphs hatch, fall and burrow underground, where they suck at the tree roots.

BY DRAWING JUICE FROM THEM. A LIQUID WHICH THEY SECRETE, CALLED HONEYDEW, CLOGS PLANT PORES AND NOURISHES FUNGI

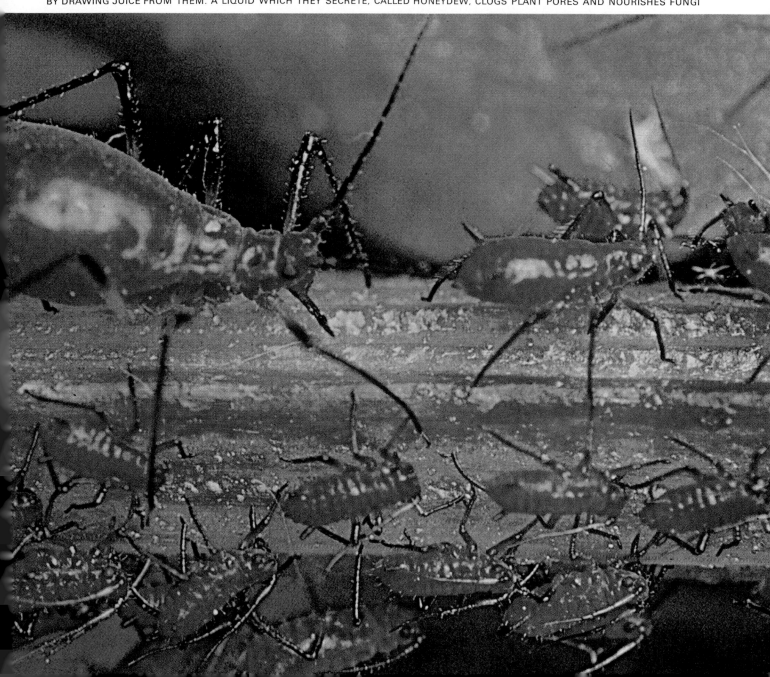

A LEAF IS CUT into pieces (*right*) by a leaf-cutter ant. Some ants do their work aloft, dropping leaf pieces to the ground. Others wait below to cart the pieces to the colony.

CARRYING A LEAF PIECE (*opposite*), an ant balances it overhead in its strong jaws. This method of carrying leaves over their heads has earned them the nickname of "parasol ants."

HEADING FOR THE NEST (*below*), a column of ants brings home a supply of leaves. Their colonies may consist of as many as 600,000 individuals living in long underground galleries.

The Ravages of Leaf-Cutter Ants

Since ants are among the most abundant of all insects, it is fortunate that few are plant pests as rapacious as the leaf-cutter ants, which can strip a tree bare in a day. They bite the leaf into handy pieces (*top*), pick them up in their long, hooked jaws (*opposite*) and move off in columns (*above*) to their nest. Leaves are necessary to the existence of the ant colony, not for food but for fertilizer. When the leaves are brought to the nest, the ants chew them into a pulp to make a kind of compost heap on which they grow their basic food—a fungus. They cultivate this fungus in large, underground "gardens." As the ant colony grows in numbers, the network of gardens increases. When a queen ant leaves to start a new colony, she carries a pellet of the fungus with her.

143

QUESTION MARK

MOURNING CLOAK

PROMETHEA

TIGER SWALLOWTAIL

SLUG CATERPILLAR

SLUG CATERPILLAR

The Voracious Caterpillars

Hardly a tree in the forest is saved from the depredations of one and sometimes several species of caterpillars. Almost endless in their variety—sluglike, spotted, striped, spiny or woolly—these creatures, the larvae of butterflies and moths, include many of the plant kingdom's worst pests. But the most formidable-looking are not necessarily the most destructive. The slug caterpillars with their spines and armor, and the brilliantly colored Promethea and tiger swallowtail

FOUR-HORNED SPHINX

SAW-TOOTHED ELM CATERPILLAR

VIRGINIA ANISOTA

OAK ANISOTA

WALNUT CATERPILLAR

YELLOW-NECKED CATERPILLAR

caterpillars feed on a wide variety of trees and shrubs, but seldom strip them enough to effect permanent damage. The question mark caterpillar, the mourning cloak, the four-horned sphinx and the saw-toothed elm caterpillar all eat elm as well as other forest leaves. Together they can give the elms a hard time, particularly the mourning cloak, which is sometimes abundant enough to wreak considerable local forest damage. The yellow-necked caterpillar can be a simi-

lar menace to apple and oak trees. Still more destructive are the Virginia Anisota, the oak Anisota and the walnut caterpillar, which periodically strip the trees bare for miles.

To make things worse, caterpillars are subject to spectacular periodic population build-ups. "Bad years" for tent caterpillars are familiar; a recent such explosion in Canada denuded trees over a 40,000-square-mile area and road traffic stalled because of the slippery masses of mashed bodies.

NONPOISONOUS

PEPPERY LACTARIUS

DELICIOUS LACTARIUS

CHANTERELLE

MARY RUSSULA

GREENISH RUSSULA

PINE CONE

POISONOUS

FLY AMANITA

FETID RUSSULA

COMMON ENTOLOMA

GREEN-SPORED MUSHROOM

EMETIC RUSSULA

The Services and

Mushrooms play a unique part in the economy of the forest. Lacking chlorophyll, they must get their food from other plants. Most mushrooms thrive on dead plants and act as "reducers." That is, they break down dead protoplasm into simple chemical substances, such as amino acids and sugars, some of which are used by the mushrooms in their own growth. The rest are liberated by decay so that green plants can use them again.

MANY CAP CLITOCYBE

COMMON MOREL

BOLETUS LUTEUS

PARASOL MUSHROOM

EDIBLE BOLETUS

COMMON MUSHROOM

the Perils of Mushrooms

The amino acids and the vitamins that the edible mushrooms above contain also make them a food source for man. But some mushrooms (*below*), for reasons that scientists do not yet understand, generate a poison named muscarine, and are highly dangerous to man. No folk legends or old wives' tales are of any help in telling good mushrooms from bad ones. The only safety lies in knowing the various species of mushrooms precisely.

DEADLY AMANITA

DESTROYING ANGEL

LARGE-SHEATHED
AMANITOPSIS

BELL-SHAPED PANAEOLUS

JACK-O'-LANTERN

COMMON STINKHORN

WAITING TICKS climb up blades of grass for a chance to attach themselves to an animal. When they bite, in order to suck blood, ticks may pass on Rocky Mountain spotted fever, whose germs they may harbor from generation to generation. Ticks are very tough. They can survive long without food, exist in water, vegetation and on the ground.

Lethal Ticks and Poisonous Leaves

Two inconspicuous foes of man in the forest are animals like ticks (*opposite*) and poisonous plants. The Rocky Mountain spotted fever tick transmits germs that cause blotches all over the body and may be fatal seven to 10 days after the bite.

Fortunately, newly developed vaccines and antibiotics now control the disease. Poisonous plants (*below*) contain a juice that inflames sensitive skins. Avoiding the plant or washing with strong soap if contact is made are the best safeguards.

WESTERN POISON OAK grows on the Pacific Coast as a shrub or vine. The leaflets are glossy.

POISON OAK, a small shrub with downy leaflets, grows in the Southeast on sandy land.

POISON IVY bears pointed leaflets in groups of three. It grows throughout most of the U.S.

POISON SUMAC, found in the East, is a five- to 10-foot tree. It usually grows in swampy areas.

8

Rise and Fall
of the Wilderness

WHEN a farmer in northern Connecticut abandons a cultivated field,
this land which was once a forest will, if left alone, follow a long trail
of changes that will bring it to forest once again. Many plants attempt to invade the untended field, but only certain ones can capture it—various
grasses, goldenrod, perhaps some berry seedlings. They all have in common
the ability to produce an abundance of seeds that germinate quickly, and
their seedlings can endure direct sunlight and drying winds. Within a few
years, the first trees appear and begin the long process of rebuilding a forest
—gray birches and little white pines that push their way through a tangle
of briers and dry, skimpy weeds. It is the white pine that dominates, for a
single mature specimen can, in a good year, flood a field with millions of
seeds—light in weight, each equipped with a little sail, easily blown by
wind. By about the 10th year of abandonment, a new forest can be plainly
seen in the making. Squat young pines and the sentinel forms of birches
now cover the field. Black-cherry seedlings grow in rings around some of

the pines, for birds have been perching in the pine branches and their droppings contain cherry seeds gathered from nearby woods.

But the pines do not last. By the time they are about 15 years old, they will have sown their own eventual destruction as dominant trees of the new forest. Their interlocking branches and evergreen foliage will have formed such a tight canopy that new pine seedlings will be unable to find enough sunlight to grow. Other kinds of trees—oaks and maples—can survive in the shade. Their seedlings can be found growing under the pines—not very vigorously, to be sure, but they have achieved a foothold on the land. Eventually, one by one, the pines succumb to the hazards of forest life—fire, wind, attack by the pine weevil, blister-rust disease, severe weather. Every pine that falls leaves an opening in the canopy, and this may be filled by one of the shade-tolerant trees that hitherto has been suppressed but now takes its place in the sun. Within 80 years after abandonment of the field there is a different kind of forest—a vigorous growth of oaks and maples with scattered remnants of the pioneer trees.

As the oaks and maples grow taller and their foliage thickens, they in turn cut off even the small amount of sunlight needed by their own seedlings. This eases the competition for other tree species that have been struggling on the forest floor, just as the oaks and maples themselves struggled under the pines decades previously. The seedlings of these trees—hemlock, beech and basswood—thrive on the dark forest floor. They grow slowly and gradually replace many of the oaks and maples that die of old age, insect plague or other forest calamities. When that happens, the hemlocks and hardwoods will grow more rapidly, annexing the space, and the forest will reach its final stage. From now on, the only seedlings that can grow in this dense forest are those of the dominant trees. A forest that has reached this sort of equilibrium is known as a climax; it often takes a forest many centuries to achieve this state.

In much of New England the climax forest is the hemlock-white pine-northern hardwoods community that so awed the pioneers. It forms a crazy-quilt pattern of alternating deciduous, coniferous and mixed forests wedged between the northern evergreens and the southern deciduous empire—stretching from northern Minnesota eastward to New England and Nova Scotia, sending a spur that dips into the Appalachians of West Virginia. Its boundaries are difficult to define exactly, for this is a zone of tension between encroaching southern species and the northern conifers.

Throughout this region, communities of plants may have different beginnings and travel different paths. In southern Connecticut, for example, the pioneering trees would probably be red cedar and in northern New England they might be red spruce. But the forest ultimately arrives at the same destination—a hemlock-white pine-northern hardwoods forest. Once plant ecologists know the complicated processes of succession for a particular region, they can reasonably well predict the succession for almost any piece of land within the region, because each kind of forest is made up of trees that require varying conditions of sunlight or shade, temperature, rainfall and soil for their growth. The abandoned Connecticut field, for example, during the centuries of succession leading to the climax, will be bombarded by countless billions of seeds blown in by the wind and carried in by birds and animals; yet only certain plants will grow, and only in a certain sequence.

In other regions of North America where different climates prevail, the climaxes are different and so are the routes traveled to achieve them. The climax forest along much of the Atlantic and Gulf of Mexico coastal plain is oak and hickory. Mesquite is a climax in many dry areas in the southwestern United States. In the Rocky Mountains, the climax that begins at timber line and extends down about 2,000 feet is composed of Engelmann spruce and Alpine fir.

As a forest passes through its successive stages, the animal life that it harbors also alters. Shortly after a field is abandoned, the field birds give way to those inhabiting brush areas. These in their turn depart when the young forest begins, and are replaced by the typically woodland species. As the forest matures, it continues to lose and attract different species of birds. In the late 1930's, the ornithologist Roger Tory Peterson made a study of the bird fauna in adjacent areas in Maine, all the way from cutover land to spruce forest. The open land was populated by savanna sparrows, song sparrows and bobolinks. In the low brush, these birds largely disappeared and were replaced by towhees, field sparrows, Nashville and chestnut-sided warblers. Where a pioneer forest had become established, ovenbirds, redstarts, red-eyed vireos and ruffed grouse arrived. As evergreens thrived and became dominant, these birds were replaced by a host of warblers (magnolia, myrtle, Blackburnian, black-throated) and the olive-backed thrush. Where the forest approached the spruce climax woodpeckers, kinglets and Cape May warblers appeared.

The ups and downs a forest endures can be pieced together from the stories told by the growth rings in tree stumps. Sometimes the rings are wide, other times so thin as to be barely distinguishable from the rings of previous years. By noting the distances between rings, one can form a picture of the growing conditions under which a tree lived, especially when the rings of certain years are correlated with known climatic data. A wide space of an inch or so between the rings may indicate very favorable weather or freedom from competition of other trees in the forest. More often, though, this space is measured in fractions of an inch, telling the story of hardships endured by the tree. A pine that grew in Idaho put on only a tenth of an inch of new growth in a century.

Fires that sweep through the forest usually do not destroy all the trees; many recover, even though their trunks are badly singed. By examination of stumps, it is often possible to learn much about past fires, when they occurred, the direction from which they came and their severity. Sometimes stumps are found in which there is an abrupt change from widely spaced to narrow rings, indicating a severe change in growing conditions that year, the result perhaps of insect or disease attacks. If the width of the rings gradually decreases over a long period of time, that tells a different story— of increasing competition from nearby trees for water, nutrients or sunlight. But if the rings on this same stump suddenly widen again, they indicate that the tree won out over the competition—that man or a natural force harvested the competing trees.

The forests growing today in the hemlock-white pine-northern hardwoods domain bear little resemblance to the primeval forests that greeted the pioneers. Three centuries of burning and logging have not only virtually destroyed the virgin examples of this kind of forest, they have also

METAMORPHOSIS OF FIELD INTO FOREST

FIRST, PIONEER PLANTS SUCH AS GRASS AND WEEDS TAKE HOLD

THEN SHRUBS AND PINES SPRING UP, CROWDING OUT GRASS AND WEEDS

THE PINES MATURE, AND DECIDUOUS SAPLINGS SPROUT IN THEIR SHADE

DECIDUOUS TREES SUPERSEDE PINES TO FORM THE FINAL CLIMAX FOREST

markedly altered the character of the forests themselves. When a forest is logged, many deciduous species send up new shoots from the old stumps, and they can continue to do so even after repeated cuttings. But the conifers growing in the same forest usually do not sprout. Cutting thus does not eliminate the deciduous trees from the forest, but it does the hemlocks or pines which must begin anew from seed. Furthermore, since sprouts grow from decapitated stumps with already established roots, they put on growth quickly, crowding out the white-pine and birch seedlings which might otherwise have gained a temporary foothold in the sunlight of the cleared area. White oaks resprout readily, but they are slow in growing. The fast growers, such as red oak, red maple and black cherry, take over out of all proportion to their original occurrence in the forest. Where the site is low and wet, the red maples may monopolize the forest entirely; on dry sunny ridges, the succession for a time will point toward almost a pure stand of oaks. The result of repeated cuttings on the forest is a long period of distortion, with certain trees growing here and there in the form of bouquets because they originated as sprouts from single stumps. Eventually, though, in many cases, the forest will return to its predestined climax.

THE climax persists so long as it is not seriously disturbed. When older hemlocks and beeches die, they are replaced by younger trees of the same species, which have been growing in the dense shade cast by their elders. But changes do occur even in the climax forest, and with greater frequency than was once believed. One thing that botanists noticed some years ago when they examined remnants of eastern virgin forest was the prevalence of stands of gigantic white pine, all of approximately the same height and growing closely together. Since the seedlings of this species require sunlight, it was clear that these larger trees could have developed only in the open, not in the middle of a climax forest. Furthermore, their equal height indicated that they had all germinated at approximately the same time. Therefore it was reasonable to assume that a hurricane might have blown down some hemlocks or deciduous trees, or that perhaps disease took its toll, or that lightning caused a fire—something that would have flooded a part of the forest floor with sunlight and allowed the white-pine seedlings to grow vigorously. Significantly, examination of the soil of these sites has disclosed layers of charcoal, making it evident that fires occurred many hundreds of years ago. Thus, the prevalence of white pine scattered throughout the primeval forest of New England attests to the fact that they were places of change even before the arrival of the white man.

Many plant ecologists believe that the stable climax forest is a rare thing. Floods, fires, erosion and earthquakes are all natural forces that can destroy forests and begin a new period of succession. Sometimes they so alter conditions that other tree species can invade the forest and an entirely new community is created. Moreover, each form of life that exists in a forest is susceptible to alteration through evolutionary changes, thus also altering the association of which it is a part.

One category of catastrophes which certainly has plagued trees for eons is diseases caused by bacteria, fungi, viruses and nematodes. Tree diseases are believed to have been less epidemic before the white man arrived, because they were kept in check by an equilibrium in the forest community. This equilibrium has been drastically altered by such practices as clearing whole forests, planting new forests of immense stands of only one or two kinds of trees and importing exotic trees, all of which weaken the bonds of the forest community. With the exotic trees have come diseases new to North America. One of these, the chestnut blight, has very nearly wiped the once abundant chestnut from the landscape. The blister rust of white pine at one time threatened to obliterate another noble species. Dutch elm disease is ravaging trees over a large part of the United States and Canada right now—and is continuing its spread.

One of the direst threats to forests today is caused by a fungus that attacks all species of oaks, the United States' best-loved tree and one of the most valuable (accounting for about a tenth of lumber production). Nearly 40 years ago, oaks in Minnesota and Wisconsin began to wilt at their topmost branches and turn bronze; the leaves gradually fell and soon the trees stood bare and lifeless. It was not until about 1942 that these symptoms were recognized as "oak wilt." By then it was too late; the disease was already entrenched and it soon spread to the magnificent oak forests of the Arkansas Ozarks, Ohio and the Smoky Mountains. Today it is present in nearly all of the states in the Midwest, and has worked east to Pennsylvania and North Carolina. Once the fungus enters an oak, there is no cure for it; no species of oak is known to be immune. The fungus spreads through the tree by way of the sapwood, growing in long strands and gradually clogging the tree's water-conducting vessels. The red-oak group (which includes red, black, scarlet, chestnut and pin oaks) is most susceptible. These trees lose all their leaves and die within a single season, sometimes in only a few weeks; even the biggest and most vigorous succumb, so completely that their stumps do not send up new sprouts. The white oaks (such as white, post and bur oaks) are more resistant to the infection, but they, too, die in a number of years.

The disease is thought to be spread primarily by insects, squirrels and birds which feed on the fungus growing on diseased trees and carry it to wounds in healthy trees. But even a healthy tree without wounds may suffer attack, for when oaks grow in dense stands the roots of neighboring trees often become joined to each other. Thus the fungus can spread through grafted roots from a single infected tree in an ever-widening circle; it may spread so rapidly that it virtually wipes out an entire stand of oak, as it has done in one state park in Iowa. The only precaution is to spot diseased trees early and then destroy them so that they will not become a focus for further infection. But this is a monumental task, and even with aerial surveys it is nearly impossible in remote wild areas where the disease may not be detected until it is too late.

THERE is a continual disturbance of forests by insects, but usually the insects are kept in check by parasites and predators or by a shortage of food. On the other hand, an imported pest, accidentally introduced, is freed from the predators in its native forests; it may multiply quickly and cause severe damage. Such a pest is the gypsy moth, which arrived in Medford, Massachusetts, in 1869, brought to North America by a French scientist who hoped to develop from it a source of silk. It promptly escaped from the laboratory and in a few years became entrenched in nearby woods and shade trees. A contemporary account described the havoc the moth caterpillars soon began to wreak: ". . . the street was black with them . . .

so thick on the trees that they were stuck together like cold macaroni. . . . The foliage was completely stripped from all the trees in the eastern part of our town, presenting an awful picture of devastation. Little was spared but the horse chestnut and the grass in the fields, though even these were eaten to some extent." Defoliation of trees retards their growth, weakens their ability to resist drought and disease and in some species it may even kill them. The white pine, for example, almost always succumbs after a single stripping of the foliage.

Since 1890 there has been program after program calculated to control or eradicate the gypsy moth, yet every year thousands of acres of forests stand leafless in June, monuments to the failure of these attempts. The gypsy moth has continued to spread throughout New England, New York, New Jersey and Pennsylvania; today it infests about 40 million acres. Entomologists have attempted to contain the pest by setting up a number of bulwarks beyond which they were determined not to let it pass. The first bulwark was the Green Mountains of Vermont and the Berkshire Hills of Massachusetts, and the entomologists marshaled their forces as a general might—seeking out pockets of resistance, constantly spraying insecticides, preventing the removal of plants from the moth zone. But the line did not hold, so they fell back on another prepared position—the Hudson River. The moths broke through that line also. Although the entomologists have a weapon that might eradicate the pest—covering the forests with a poisonous blanket of insecticides sprayed from aircraft—they are afraid to use it. They are sensitive to the warnings of ecologists that, in addition to eradicating the gypsy moth, the spray would eradicate many other links in the forest web of life as well, and perhaps in the end bring greater destruction to the forests than that caused by the moths.

In some kinds of forest—because of the prevailing climate, the inflammability of the vegetation and other factors—fires are common, and were so long before the white man arrived in the New World. Early explorers of North America wrote of traveling for days through the smoke from distant fires. Examination of growth rings of some redwoods of California has revealed an average of about four fires a century during the more than thousand-year life of the stand. In other kinds of forests, stumps tell a story of fires every few years. Many of these were probably caused by lightning, but others by Indians who burned forests to clear land and to drive out game, and who appear to have taken no more care in extinguishing campfires than men do today.

A fire does more than kill or damage trees already growing; it changes the whole forest for decades to come. By removing the layer of litter from the forest floor, killing seedlings and weakening the dominant trees, it creates conditions favorable for certain trees usually very different from those originally growing. These trees—notably aspen, pitch pine, jack pine and lodgepole pine—thrive on bare soil and full sunlight, and depend largely on fire to survive. In northern Minnesota and Wisconsin can be seen today immense forests consisting almost solely of jack pine. But before this land was pioneered, jack pine was an insignificant member of the forest community; the forest was similar in composition to the white-pine and northern hardwoods forest of New England. Lumbermen removed the giant white pines, and the slash left by the logging operation became

SOME USES OF LUMBER IN THE UNITED STATES

(Figures are in thousands of board feet consumed per year)

All manufacturing	11,742,902
Furniture	1,853,520
Shipping containers and crates	1,170,086
Hardwood flooring	1,144,141
Prefabricated wood products	824,273
Trailer homes	236,056
Toys and sporting goods	140,320
Refrigeration machinery	120,525
Partitions, venetian blinds and shades	107,846
Morticians' goods	81,510
Ship and boat building	74,726
Cutlery, hand tools and general hardware	51,998
Musical instruments	51,376
Railroad equipment	43,963
Signs and advertising displays	35,832
Farm machinery	35,658
Household electric appliances	24,549
Truck trailers	18,950
Brooms and brushes	8,710
Office, computing and accounting machines	7,043
Matches	560

a tinderbox; infernos swept through the remaining hardwoods, killing practically all the trees. But the fires were a blessing to the jack pines, since their cones differ from those of most other conifers. Under normal conditions, the cones of jack pine remain tightly closed and hang on the tree; the seeds inside remain viable for years. But when heated, as by a fire, they open, scattering immense quantities of seeds onto a bed of ashes from which other competing species have been eliminated. One study of fires in Minnesota revealed that there might be as few as half a dozen jack pines to an acre of forest before a fire, but afterward those few trees might cover their acre with 15,000 to 20,000 seedlings.

Similarly, in the Pacific Northwest are great stands of towering Douglas firs, so mighty and abundant that it would appear they must be the dominant trees of the region. They are not, for shade-tolerant hemlocks and cedars replace the aging Douglas firs as the climax vegetation, since the fir seedlings cannot survive in the dense shade cast by mature trees. But fire delays the achievement of the climax by making openings in the dark forest in which fir seed from nearby stands can take hold and overtop the cedar and hemlock seedlings.

INSECTS, disease and fire are natural disturbers of the forest succession. But in the past few hundred years a new disturbance, civilized man, has intruded in the forests of North America and in this brief time has changed them more rapidly than all the other forces of nature combined. Not only has modern man affected the forest by the obvious means of clearing, logging and burning, but his effect has been more subtle in altering the invisible bonds between living things. Examples of injudicious tampering with the forest community are many—and well known, because they usually ended in well-publicized disasters. But they are best illustrated by what happened many years ago in the Kaibab forest of northern Arizona when an attempt was made to redesign and improve on the well-knit fabric of forest life.

Before it was tampered with, the Kaibab was a storybook forest of ponderosa pine, Douglas fir, white fir, blue and Engelmann spruce. One visitor described it glowingly in 1882: "We, who through successive summers have wandered through its forests and parks, have come to regard it as the most enchanting region it has ever been our privilege to visit." It was also the home of the Rocky Mountain mule deer and a hunting ground for Indians who gathered every autumn and killed deer for meat and to obtain skins for winter clothing and trading. The forest also supported a population of mountain lions, coyotes and timber wolves that kept the deer population within bounds.

Then, in 1906, President Theodore Roosevelt decreed that the Kaibab be made a national game preserve. In order to build up the herds, deer hunting was prohibited in the preserve and government hunters set about systematically eliminating the predators upon the deer. Within the next 25 years, the deer's natural enemies were virtually eradicated—at least 6,250 mountain lions, coyotes, wolves and bobcats were killed. Before the vermin-control program began, there were about 4,000 deer in the Kaibab. Within a dozen years, the supervisor of the forest warned that the deer were increasing rapidly and that the supply of small trees, shrubs and saplings they used as food was declining.

SOME USES OF PULPWOOD IN THE UNITED STATES

(Figures are in thousands of tons consumed per year)

Paperboard containers	15,634
Newsprint	2,010
Book paper	1,912
Construction boards	1,782
Writing paper	1,771
Construction paper	1,350
Paper bags	1,247
Toilet paper	886
Wrapping paper	537
Paper towels	504
Rayon	387
Facial tissues	255
Napkins	232

SOME OTHER WOOD USES IN THE UNITED STATES

(Unless otherwise indicated, figures are in millions of cubic feet used per year)

Fuel wood	2,008
Mine timbers	81
Cooperage (barrels, kegs and tubs)	73
Piling for docks and building foundations	28
Turpentine	645,000 barrels
Christmas trees	40,000,000 trees
Maple syrup	1,700,000 gallons
Maple sugar	168,000 pounds
Poles for power, telephone and telegraph lines	6,500,000 poles
Fence posts	306,000,000 posts

Scant attention was paid to the warnings, since obviously an increase in deer numbers was what had been intended by the predator-eradication program. By 1924, the deer herds had increased fantastically; some estimates put them near 100,000. That was the high point for the deer. They were now threatened with mass starvation, having already eaten nearly every plant and tree they could reach. From then on the population collapsed. A contemporary account reported that deer perished by the thousands and "those that lived ate every leaf and twig till the whole country looked as though a swarm of locusts had swept through it, leaving the range (except for the taller shrubs and trees) torn, gray, stripped and dying." Hunting of deer was permitted once again, and although it caused a slight decrease in deer numbers, most of the decrease resulted from starvation and disease, which killed 60 per cent of the deer herd in two winters. By 1930, the herd had plummeted to about 20,000 animals. By 1942 it was down to 8,000.

Witness the results of 35 years of unwise tampering with the Kaibab: in 1906 it was a relatively stable community of life that supported a healthy population of about 4,000 deer in addition to those killed by Indians, settlers and predatory animals. By 1942, there were 8,000 sickly deer and the bonds of the forest had been shattered. Certain plant species, such as willows and raspberries, had been virtually eradicated by the deer. Growth of young aspen had been halted over a period of almost 20 years; in some sections all reproduction of cliff rose had stopped during this period; the vast majority of the firs, spruces and pines had suffered severe damage. By thinning out the trees and shrubs, the deer had favored the growth of certain grasses and herbs which they do not usually select as food; these plants were also aided by the increase of space in which to grow, and by the decrease of shade and root competition from the species the deer did browse. As a result, the forest composition changed in favor of the grasses and one authority stated that if the deer had remained numerous, the area might have changed from a woodland to a tree-dotted grassland, held in this sub-climax state by the browsing animals.

THE Kaibab is a striking example of the folly of working against natural principles of the forest, instead of *with* them—as has been done at Isle Royale National Park in Lake Superior. Moose arrived there in 1912, probably having swum from Canada. Conditions were ideal, and they multiplied to a population of over 1,500, overbrowsing the woods to the point where they became so weakened that their numbers plummeted to only a few hundred by the mid-1930s. As the young trees began to grow again, the moose herd built up once more. But then, in the late 1940s, wolves arrived on the island, probably crossing the ice in winter. For the past several years, the moose numbers have become stabilized at about 600, despite the birth of approximately 160 young each year. That is because the wolves cull out an equal number of aged and sick moose. Because man did not interfere in the intricate predator-prey relationships of this forest, a balance has been achieved. The moose herd remains stable in numbers, well fed and healthy; the wolf predators have a constant food supply and seem even to maintain a balance of their own numbers; the forest supports both predator and prey, renews itself and is in better condition than it was before the wolves arrived.

THE BOOLE BIG TREE IN SEQUOIA NATIONAL FOREST, SHOWN WITH 86 PEOPLE AT ITS BASE, IS NAMED FOR THE LOGGER WHO SAVED IT

The Ravaged Forests

For 300 years the virgin forest covering the United States has fallen before the march of the farmer, the logger, the industrialist and the forest fire. Two thirds of an estimated original 8,125,000 million board feet of wood was consumed, leaving 200 million acres of treeless land, much of it eroded and burned, so that by 1920, 80 million acres were useless even for crops.

GIRDLED TREES rise starkly on cleared land in the Blue Ridge Mountains. As fast as the trees died, they were used for fencing and fuel, and the open land was then planted in corn.

"STUMP-FARM" HOMESTEADERS STAND BEFORE A CABIN OF HAND-HEWN CEDAR SHAKES ON WASHINGTON'S SKAGIT RIVER IN 1904.

GNAWING EROSION threatens the footings of both house and shed on this Mississippi farm. Thirty years previously, this gully had been a wagon road on wooded hills cleared for crops.

THEY PLANTED CROPS AMONG THE STUMPS AND ALSO WORKED FOR LOGGING OUTFITS THAT FELLED THE GROVES OF DOUGLAS FIR

HORSE AND RIDER easily fit in the undercut in this sequoia (*right*). About a thousand cubic feet were chopped, enough for a house, if sawed into lumber from a saw-timber tree.

SURE-FOOTED OXEN haul ponderosa pine logs to a mill in the Pacific Northwest. Yoked in pairs, often 12 pairs per wagon, oxen were the logger's power prior to the donkey engine. They also hauled logs on a "skid road" greased with fish oil.

THE "BUCKER" OF A LOGGING CREW stands on a moss-covered Douglas fir (*left*), 10 feet thick. Buckers used two-man saws called "misery whips," often 12 feet long, for the strenuous work of cutting felled trees into marketable lengths.

163

SMELTING OPERATIONS destroyed the forest and poisoned the soil around this desolate homesite in the Copper Basin of Tennessee. Conservation practices may bring it back.

LOGGING, followed by erosion, decimated this Colorado forest. Plundered by loggers and later swept by fire, this landscape has since been reforested by the U.S. Forest Service.

WARFARE AND FIRE ravaged the Hürtgen Forest in Germany, a World War II battleground, shown after a fire in 1947 which was ignited by ammunition left from the battle.

A FOREST FIRE BLAZES ACROSS WOODED RIDGES IN CALIFORNIA. IN THE U.S., NINE OUT OF 10 SUCH FIRES ARE CAUSED BY MAN

A BRIGHT CARPET of vine maples in fall glows among the old ashes and charred snags of the huge Yacolt Burn, scene of a severe forest fire in southern Washington. The small vine maple of the Pacific Northwest quickly covers logged land and old burns, spreading branches on the ground and around stumps. The Yacolt fire destroyed 239,920 acres of

forest in 1902, lifting clouds of smoke so dense that they caused cities of the Pacific Northwest to light lamps throughout the "dark day" of September 12. Of the major North American forest fires in the last century, the worst was the Peshtigo fire in Wisconsin and Michigan in 1871, when 3,780,000 acres of timber were burned and 1,638 lives lost.

9

Forests
of the Future

IN June 1853, the New England naturalist and inhabiter of wild places,
Henry David Thoreau, jotted in his journal: "If a man walks in the
woods for love of them . . . for half his days, he is esteemed a loafer; but
if he spends his whole day as a speculator, shearing off those woods, he is
esteemed industrious and enterprising—making earth bald before its time."
A revolutionary idea; for although western man has been singing romantic
hymns about the forest since antiquity, he has also regarded it as something
hostile, to be cleared and burned. The decimation of forests was well under
way in classical times, for Homer described the noise of battle as "the din
of woodcutters in the glades of a mountain."

The mutilation of the woods of the New World began with the arrival
of the first settlers. Farsighted William Penn insisted that in lands granted
by him an acre should be left in forest for every five acres cleared but
he was an exception. Trees were overabundant and free for the taking;
forests harbored Indians and wild beasts, and covered land needed for

crops, so they were best cleared. The first wave of loggers to hit the woods took out the high-value trees for shipmasts and naval timbers. The second wave took the walnuts and similar species valued for their grain; the less valuable species such as oaks and maples were passed by. Finally the woods were clean-shaven—scalped for firewood, worked over for fence posts and bridge supports—and cattle were allowed to scavenge the denuded land.

The long cross-country trek of the lumbermen began. By the early 1880s they had chopped their way through much of New England and the wood pinch was already being felt; as early as 1804 a Massachusetts society offered prizes for tree planting. State after state in the East gazed at the stark woodlands, and leading citizens began to cry out for conservation. But the lumbermen could not hear—they had already left to cull over the forests of western New York and Ohio. Michigan and Wisconsin were largely denuded by 1890. As virgin timber from the lake states neared depletion, the tide of the lumbermen split—some kept going west to the great conifers of the Rockies, others veered southward to the pine stands.

By the time Theodore Roosevelt became president, the lumbermen had chopped their way to the vast virgin forests of the Pacific Coast and there was nowhere else to go. When Roosevelt appointed a committee to report to him on what had happened to the nation's resources, this is the picture that emerged: each year reckless methods of logging were wasting a fourth of the timber cut. Stripping of tree cover was dangerously reducing the water-holding capacity of the soil: headwaters were eroding, stream banks once held by trees were washing away. Slash left on the ground after logging was a tinderbox and fires were roaring through the ravaged land. Logging up to this point had been, like mining, extracting a nonrenewable resource rather than wisely harvesting a renewable crop.

The nation gazed at the bare ribs of the land and mourned the loss. But there was one man, Gifford Pinchot, who had a vision that the scars could be healed. He became Chief Forester to Theodore Roosevelt and the two of them brought conservation to America. They organized commissions to study the forests, they held investigations, they issued shocking reports. Forestry schools were established, textbooks were written on the new science of forest management; a strong start was made in fire control. In only nine years, Roosevelt deposited in national forests a total of 119 million acres on which a system of management has been developed that is today a model of wise use.

So in our time, there has developed a new breed of lumberman—he carries a forestry textbook instead of an ax. He is using the tools of modern science to juggle succession, to breed superior trees, to ally himself with insects to fight other insects. Instead of "cutting out and getting out," he tends trees that his grandchildren will see in their prime; his landholdings are so managed as to restore wildlife, to maintain the water-holding capacity of the soil, to provide green belts for campers and hunters. When a modern logger cuts over an area, seed trees are left to reforest and heal the wounds. After three centuries of plunder and greedy cuttings, the tide has turned: instead of ever-shrinking woodlands, American forests are now growing more timber each year than is being cut.

National forests—there are now 155 of them covering 181 million acres in 39 states and Puerto Rico—have been established by Congress not only to ensure a future timber supply but also to regulate stream flow. Good forest soil is a natural reservoir for rain water and snow melt. A stream in a forest runs clear and steady—rather than being murky and undependable, rising rapidly after a rain, then shrinking to a trickle. That is because the solid earth of most forest soil is not solid at all—about half of "soil" is made up of air, water and the multitude of living things that inhabit it. The fine pores between the grains hold water like a sponge. One study made in Ohio revealed that a deciduous forest held 14 times more water than an adjacent open field.

A GOOD illustration of the effect of vegetation on water is found in the histories of two towns in Utah. Farmington and Centerville were among the earliest Mormon settlements, both located along the eastern shore of Great Salt Lake. The citizens of these towns built irrigation canals to carry water to their fields from the Wasatch Mountains looming behind them. For decades the towns grew and prospered as the streams that brought their water gave a dependable, clean flow.

Then one day a cloudburst sent an avalanche of mud and rocks rushing down the mountains toward Farmington. Much of the town was inundated, highways blocked, orchards destroyed; some of the best farms were buried under six feet of mud. Every summer thereafter violent storms brought muddy water and finally a major devastation that paralyzed the entire area. A commission of scientists was appointed to investigate the sudden rebellion of the streams. Their conclusion: summer storms were no heavier than they had been in preflood days. But what had changed were the mountain soils; once covered by trees and shrubs, these headwater areas had been so denuded by the grazing of livestock and man-caused fires that the soil could no longer soak up the rain. At one stream an intense rain produced up to 160 times more runoff water than it did at a nearby stream mantled with vegetation.

But what about neighboring Centerville? It received nearly the same rainfall and its water supply came from the same mountains—yet instead of bringing floods, its creeks continued to flow clear and steady. The reason was the foresight of the people of Centerville. They had purchased or leased the forests and grazing lands in the mountains from which water drained into their creeks; they had kept cattle off it and prevented fires.

So foresters began to remake the Farmington creeks, starting high up in the headwaters where the floods began. They built expensive engineering works, replanted trees and grasses, eliminated grazing and took strict fire-prevention measures. At heavy cost, much of the work was completed by 1936. Since the reclothing, these slopes have been assaulted by more than 300 summer storms, but no floods have occurred on the treated creeks.

The new breed of men in the woods is bringing scientific technique to bear on every phase of forest life from seeding to harvest. Geneticists are combing the woods in search of the most vigorous trees to be used as sources of seeds for new plantings. A stock of such superior seed trees has been accumulated in the south, a warehouse for 300 million future trees which will grow taller and straighter and be better able to resist insects and diseases than others of their kind.

Geneticists are also trying to tailor-make trees, to develop strains that will grow best in particular areas and sites. By selecting male cones from

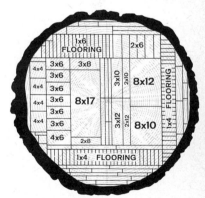

CROSSCUT OF FIR shows how a log can be sawed into lumber. Heavy structural timbers are taken from the center of the tree, and thinner boards and flooring from the edges.

superior trees and spraying the pollen onto female cones, they can improve on nature by creating new strains and hybrids. Already being developed are disease-resistant pines, spruces that grow faster, maple trees with sweeter sap, chestnut trees that can withstand the blight. A world-wide catalog of "super" trees and their exact locations is being accumulated. Sweden's lists about 3,000 selected for outstanding growth.

Few woods have suffered greater decimation than those of Georgia. The natural climax forest over much of Georgia is oak and hickory. But when the land was cleared for cotton and tobacco several hundred years ago, the soil was quickly depleted and, lacking its forest cover, began to erode. As farmer after farmer gave up the land in disgust and moved westward, it gradually reverted to forest, usually extensive areas of pines with some hardwoods. But these hardwoods were not the same valuable species nor did they have the same quality of tree as the ones that had grown in the virgin soil. However, in recent years great strides have been taken toward rebuilding forests finer than those met by the pioneers.

T HE work being done in Georgia is intricate. It involves juggling tree species to delay the natural succession to hardwoods by suppressing them and encouraging the faster-growing pines. But this must not be overdone; broad-leaved trees give many benefits in a forest. For one thing, they have a favorable influence on the soil, returning their leaves to it much more rapidly, the decomposed matter mixing with the mineral soil and making it better able to hold water. Pine needles, on the other hand, are low in nutrients and high in lignin, and they decompose very slowly. So it is necessary to determine not only the proportion of broad-leaved trees that should be left in the forest, but also which species are the best for soil-building. The worthless hardwoods are eliminated. Trained men carrying immense hypodermic syringes or growth-regulating chemicals now take to the woods. These chemicals spur the trees to sudden growth so rapid that the plant tissue is killed.

The old race of husky lumberjacks, proud of their skill with hand tools and their gimcrack sawmills, is now dying out. They used to work miles from a paved road, cutting the logs by "chip-chopping," skidding them down slopes with the aid of horses and in the spring bringing down the drive—"walking down the middle of the river," they called it. Instead of axes and the backbreaking two-man crosscut saw, gasoline-powered chain saws are now used. Instead of skidding, logs are carried to the bottoms of slopes by immense sky lines that, like ski tows, lift the trunks high above the ground. Now there are tractors with hydraulically operated arms that gather up wood a cord at a time as easily as a boy picks up a handful of kindling. At the mill, machines with giant claws lift up a dozen logs without a groan and stack them. A multitude of uses, unknown only a few decades ago, are being found for these logs, including livestock feed and stronger structural beams fastened together with new glues.

Meanwhile the war against insects and infection goes on. Today many forest insects are being controlled in massive assaults by airplanes flying over the treetops and spraying lethal chemicals. But forest entomologists are also allying themselves with disease-producing microorganisms and pitting insect against insect. When a pest is introduced accidentally to North America, it is usually freed from the natural control of parasites

A CHRONOLOGY OF THE DECLINE OF THE AMERICAN FOREST

Pre-1600   Approximately 1,030,000,000 acres in forest. An Indian population of less than one million makes limited use of wood for fuel, weapons and housing but also destroys large areas of forest each year by setting fires to flush out game. Heavy grazing by buffaloes helps keep in grassland many areas which would normally be covered with trees.

1700   1,025,000,000 acres in forest. White settlement started at Jamestown in 1607. Population is now 250,000, mostly on the Eastern Seaboard. Clearing of the forest for agriculture, fuel and building begins. Export of lumber products, particularly naval stores, is heavy.

1800   One billion acres in forest. Population is 5,297,000, and in the East there is already a wood shortage near large cities. The American West just beyond the Appalachians is opening up and vast acreages are being cleared for farmland. Many homes and farms in New England are already being abandoned and the lumber industry is moving westward with the settlers. In 1831 the government forbids the cutting of trees on federally owned lands.

1850   900 million acres in forest. Population is 23,250,000, more than seven million of whom are living west of the Appalachians. In the 1860s the Civil War causes heavy demands for wood in both the North and the South, and large forest areas are damaged in the fighting. In 1872, Yellowstone, the first national park, is established. The Timber Culture Act of 1873 offers free land to settlers who plant trees on 40 acres of each 160-acre claim. In 1898 Gifford Pinchot, America's pioneer conservationist, heads the Agriculture Department's Forestry Division, which is to become the U.S. Forest Service.

and insect predators that existed in its native habitat. World-wide searches have been made for these natural enemies; they have been imported, reared by the millions and released to restore the balance of nature.

Like other forms of life, insects are subject to diseases. Many of these diseases pinpoint their target, attacking perhaps one or two species of insect but causing no damage to the rest of the forest community. But among the species they do attack, they sometimes cause epidemics and virtually wipe out entire insect populations; their constant inroads are what prevent catastrophic build-ups of many insect species. In recent years there has been a quickening of the pace to control harmful insects by artificially spreading their diseases. A notable success has been the campaign against the European spruce sawfly. When first detected on this continent, the sawfly was already causing severe damage over several thousand square miles of Canadian forests. There being no European parasites or predators to keep its number down, scientists were hard pressed to keep it from covering the entire continent, until entomologists were sent to Europe where they captured a number of the sawfly's parasitic enemies. These were reared in laboratories and liberated throughout the spruce woods. Within only a few years, a check revealed that the parasites had become successfully established and were killing numerous sawflies.

Also discovered was a startling fact—the sawflies were falling prey to a virus disease that apparently had been introduced along with the parasites from Europe. Soon the virus took over the job, killing about 99 per cent of the larvae and ending the outbreak. Forest entomologists hastened the natural spread of the disease by taking it to new areas where it had not yet become established. Spruce sawflies continue to remain common insects in Canada, but nowhere do they escape the disease in sufficient numbers to cause great damage.

Alerted to the potentialities of control of insects by disease, Canadian entomologists turned their attention to another sawfly introduced from Europe, this one attacking pine trees. The pest had spread through most of southwestern Ontario by 1949 and immediately began building up a large and hungry population. Insects were trapped and carefully examined to see if any of them was suffering from diseases. None was, so a call was sent to Sweden requesting live specimens infected by a virus known to attack the insect in Europe. The order was filled, the virus cultured in the laboratory and sprayed by airplane over woods infested by the insects. Within only a few weeks, most of the sawflies in the sprayed area had fallen before the disease. Now the virus is produced in quantity and distributed to wood-lot owners in Canada and the United States. It has been so successful that it has generally replaced insecticides in combating this dangerous pest.

WHETHER man will ever succeed in completely controlling the forces that govern the forest—and how long it will take to do so—are imponderable questions. In some areas of the globe, where the forest fabric has been so ripped apart that deserts now prevail, it is nearly beyond the imagination to believe that these lands will ever be clothed with greenery again. Yet, even in Copper Basin of east Tennessee—which was turned into a moonscape by logging, burning and the poisoning of the soil by fumes from copper smelters—the first steps have been taken in mantling the

FOREST DECLINE (CONTINUED)

1900 800 million acres in forest. Population is 76 million, with immigration reaching as high as 400,000 persons a year. Much of the virgin pine forest of the lake states has been completely cleared, and the center of lumbering moves first to the South and then to the Far West. In 1909 lumber production reaches an all-time high of 46 billion board feet. In 1911 the first federal legislation providing protection of watersheds of navigable rivers is passed.

1918 608 million acres in forest. Heavy demands created by World War I reduce the forest acreage in America to the all-time low. To prevent waste, Congress passes the Clarke-McNary Act, which provides for effective fire control on federal forest lands. At this time between 30 and 40 million acres of timber are being burned each year.

1938 771 million acres in forest. Population is 132 million. For the first time since 1600, total forest land increases. The depression reduces the cutting of timber, and heavy population movement from farm to cities permits large cultivated acreage to revert to forest. The federal Civilian Conservation Corps plants 2,356,000,000 young trees.

1945 765 million acres in forest. World War II causes another decrease in forest land. During the war and postwar period, western forests supply 55 per cent of the total American lumber production, the South 35 per cent and the North 10 per cent.

1960 773,400,000 acres in forest. Peace and intensified conservation practices by government and private lumber companies strike a balance for the first time between annual wood cut and annual wood growth. The American forest begins a new era of expansion.

land with vegetation once more. In the Sahara a British forester, Sir Richard St. Barbe Baker, has set up an international organization to reverse the march of the desert by planting trees. Some of the starkest landscapes in the world, places in the Middle East that have not seen forests in thousands of years, are being planted with Australian eucalyptus through the assistance of the United Nations Food and Agriculture Organization. Man the destroyer has in this century become man the erector of new green mansions.

MEANWHILE, the forests themselves continue to undergo changes largely beyond man's control. They are on the move today, marching northward before our eyes as the climate continues to warm. In the last half century, temperatures in parts of the North Temperate Zone have increased from two to five degrees. Glaciers are shrinking noticeably: in Alaska, the vast Muir glacier retreated about 13 and a half miles between 1899 and 1946. The thickness of the Greenland icecap is gradually shrinking. The tree line in Finland has been moving northward into the tundra; annual rings are showing a quickening of growth in Scandinavia. Trees are growing north of where they have never grown before in history. Wildlife is on the march also. About 15 species of birds, regarded as southern only a half century ago, now breed in Canada.

Although it is still largely speculation, a number of authorities believe that the general warming trend is responsible for an agony many forest trees are presently undergoing. Some of North America's noblest trees are in trouble and no insect, disease or other apparent cause can be found. Oaks, maples, pines, birches and sweet gums are only a few of the species that have been suffering a major decline in recent years. There have been spectacular diebacks of birch in both New England and Nova Scotia. In the latter, a survey over a recent 30-year period showed an average temperature increase of two to three degrees. Slight as this rise may seem, it is enough to affect the tree's hardiness by altering its normal rates of photosynthesis, respiration and absorption of minerals. It could also upset the equilibrium of microorganisms and insects in the soil. For example, the prevalence of a disease of quaking aspen near the Canadian border is only half as great as it is 100 miles farther south, although there are no known differences between the two places except for the fact that one is slightly warmer than the other and hence possibly more hospitable to a disease microbe.

But the species a forest loses by a change of climate are replaced by a natural introduction of species unable to live there before. Meanwhile the current diebacks are being intensively studied. To the woods-wise naturalist, they signal but another change in the shifting forest scene that has been going on since the Devonian period—the rise and fall of species, the building of new living communities, the taking of new evolutionary highways. What will these future forests look like? Many botanists can foresee no major improvements over the angiosperms. Yet, there is a possible human parallel. In 1844, the U.S. Commissioner of Patents stated that the arts and sciences had so developed that "it taxes our credulity" to believe that there would be many more new inventions. He could no more visualize atomic energy and space satellites than a modern woods-walker can foresee the evolutionary inventions of a future world.

YEAR-OLD SEEDLINGS GROW IN A WISCONSIN FOREST. IN FIVE YEARS, IF CONDITIONS ARE GOOD, THEY WILL BE FIVE FEET HIGH

The Forest Returns

A new philosophy rules in the woodlands that cover almost a third of the nation. Commercial timber, once victim of "cut out and get out" loggers, is now farmed as a crop, scientifically bred, nurtured and harvested. Under proper management, forest prospects are bright. Although 14.1 million cubic feet are removed annually, the growth each year is 25 per cent greater.

BLOCK CUTTING OF THE FOREST ON A TREE FARM IN WASHINGTON LEAVES SURROUNDING TREES TO RESEED LOGGED AREAS. THE SCARS

The Changing Timber Industry and Its New Techniques

The nation's forests have become a long-term investment instead of a one-time crop, and sustained yields are now ensured by scientific study and better logging practices. Foresters today depend on four main harvesting methods. The first, called clear cutting, removes all trees in a large area, which can then be reforested only by planting seedlings. Block cutting (*above*) consists of clearing sections of about 100 acres, leaving the

surrounding trees to do the work of reseeding. Both systems work well for species that need full sun for growth, notably jack pine and Douglas fir. The third method is the seed tree system, widely employed in southern pine forests. It leaves about half a dozen healthy trees on each logged acre to reseed the land. The fourth method, selective cutting, is best for shade-tolerant species. These harvesting techniques have been

A TREE FELLER cuts a six-foot Douglas fir with a gasoline-powered chain saw in two minutes. The same job done with the old two-man bucksaw would have taken 20 minutes.

FLATCARS move a load of timber in Washington. These logs were snaked out of the forest with tractors, then floated downriver to a railhead and are now en route to a sawmill.

WERE MADE BY LOGS DRAGGED TO A CENTRAL LOADING POINT

notably successful for the fast-growing trees that are the main suppliers of the pulp industry, like the southern pines, which are ready for cutting only 30 years after seeding. They are not so successful, however, at getting a sustained yield from the slow-growing hardwood forests, where selective cutting, with its lower profit margin, is the best logging method. Maple, for example, may take 80 years to grow to commercial size.

ARTIFICIAL POLLINATION of ponderosa pines is achieved by enclosing female conelets in bags with cellophane windows so that stray pollen cannot reach them, and then injecting selected "superior" pollen into the bags with a hypodermic syringe. To produce the maximum number of fertile seeds, conelets are pollinated several times a season.

HYBRID PINE, at left above, is bigger and brawnier, due to artificial pollination, than the white pines beside it. All are seedlings from the same tree and all are five years old.

SQUIRREL-CAGE SEPARATOR shakes seeds from cones. For precise genetic studies, the individual seeds are removed by hand. The cones are first kiln-dried to loosen seeds.

Bigger and Better Trees

Forest management can do much to restore the past imbalance between logging and tree growth in American forests, but there is another disturbing factor in the long-range picture: recent industrial estimates warn that the U.S. demand for timber may double within the next 50 years. There are two ways to meet this problem. The tree itself can be better utilized. In 1900 only a third of a tree found its way into useful products. Today nearly three fourths of a tree does. As methods are developed for the use of sawdust, bark and other throw-away parts, virtually the entire tree will soon be useful.

Trees themselves can be improved. They can be made to grow faster, taller, thicker and even straighter through hybridization, the artificial development of new species which have these features and which are also more resistant to diseases and insects. Hybrid trees are created by artificial pollination at stations like the Institute of Forest Genetics at Placerville, California, where the pictures on these pages were taken. Once a superior hybrid is developed it can become a factory for the production of "super" seed which is collected mechanically from the pine cones, chemically treated to minimize losses to fungi and animals, and sown by helicopter.

EXPERIMENTAL NURSERY contains beds of pine seedlings of different ages. Hybrid strains are developed here and checked for growth and hardiness under varying conditions.

A FOREST GENETICIST fills vials with pine pollen from dried catkins funneled from the bag above him. Specimens are then sealed and stored for future pollination projects.

A Vast Industry and Its Multitude of Products

Each American uses an annual average of 470 pounds of paper and 205 board feet of lumber. This vast appetite for wood, paper and forest products in the United States, valued at $29 billion per year, is fed by an industry that operates 32,000 sawmills, 360 pulp mills, 800 paper mills and 511 plywood and veneer mills. About 49 per cent of the timber harvest goes into saw logs for building and industry, 23 per cent into pulpwood, 5 per cent into fuel, 8 per cent into veneer and plywood and 15 per cent—mainly logging residues—is put to various industrial uses. And the demand for paper products, like those produced in the Louisiana paperboard mill shown below, increases each year. This mill's machines take off the bark, chip the wood, grind it and dry it for the rollers that will smooth it into paper. Machines in similar plants can endlessly roll out newsprint at 20 miles an hour—as they must, since an American Sunday paper of 128 pages and a million circulation needs about 140 acres of pulpwood timber for one edition.

STACK UPON STACK OF PULP LOGS, FROM 500,000 NEARBY ACRES, AWAIT THE PROCESSING THAT WILL TURN THEM INTO KRAFT

THE ANNUAL YIELD of a 10-acre pine wood lot is stacked in this log pile: 4,853 board feet of saw logs (*foreground*), then 4.5 cords of pulpwood and 2.5 cords for chemical processing.

PAPER IN THIS LOUISIANA MILL. FOUR OTHER PLANTS ON THE SAME FACTORY SITE CONVERT THE PAPER INTO PACKAGING PRODUCTS

Bibliography

Plant Anatomy and Physiology

Bonner, James, and Arthur W. Galston, *Principles of Plant Physiology*. W. H. Freeman, 1952.

Croker, W., and L. V. Barton, *Physiology of Seeds*. Ronald Press, 1957.

Cronquist, Arthur, *Introductory Botany*. Harper & Row, 1961.

Eames, A. J., and L. H. MacDaniels, *An Introduction to Plant Anatomy* (2nd ed.). McGraw-Hill, 1947.

† *Plant Life*. A Scientific American book. Simon and Schuster, 1949.

Transeau, Edgar, H. C. Sampson and L. H. Tiffany, *Textbook of Botany* (rev. ed.). Harper & Row, 1953.

Plant Ecology and Geography

Braun, E. Lucy, *Deciduous Forests of Eastern North America*. Blakiston, 1950.

Cain, Stanley A., *Foundations of Plant Geography*. Harper & Row, 1944.

Good, R., *The Geography of Flowering Plants*. Longmans Green, London, 1953.

Neal, Ernest, *Woodland Ecology*. Harvard University Press, 1958.

Oosting, Henry J., *The Study of Plant Communities* (2nd ed.). W. H. Freeman, 1956.

Polunin, Nicholas, *Introduction to Plant Geography*. McGraw-Hill, 1960.

Richards, Paul W., *The Tropical Rain Forest*. University Press, Cambridge, 1952.

Watts, May Theilgaard, *Reading the Landscape*. Macmillan, 1957.

Weaver, J. E., and F. E. Clements, *Plant Ecology* (2nd ed.). McGraw-Hill, 1938.

Paleontology

Andrews, Henry N. Jr., *Studies in Paleobotany*. John Wiley & Sons, 1961.

Arnold, Chester A., *An Introduction to Paleobotany*. McGraw-Hill, 1947.

Dunbar, Carl O., *Historical Geology* (2nd ed.). John Wiley & Sons, 1960.

Fenton, Carroll Lane, and Mildred Adams Fenton, *The Fossil Book*. Doubleday, 1958.

Seward, A. C., *Plant Life Through the Ages* (2nd ed.). Hafner, 1959.

Animal Life in the Forest

Allee, W. C., A. E. Emerson, O. Park, T. Park and K. P. Schmidt, *Principles of Animal Ecology*. Saunders, 1949.

Allen, Arthur A., *The Book of Bird Life*. D. Van Nostrand, 1961.

Berger, Andrew J., *Bird Study*. John Wiley & Sons, 1961.

Bourlière, François, *The Natural History of Mammals*. Alfred A. Knopf, 1964.

Drimmer, Frederick, ed., *Animal Kingdom* (3 vols.). Doubleday, 1954.

Gilliard, E. Thomas, *Living Birds of the World*. Doubleday, 1958.

Hesse, R., W. C. Allee and K. P. Schmidt, *Ecological Animal Geography* (2nd ed.). John Wiley & Sons, 1951.

Klots, Alexander B., and Elsie B., *Living Insects of the World*. Doubleday, 1959.

Murphy, Robert C., and Dean Amadon, *Land Birds of America*. McGraw-Hill, 1953.

Oliver, James A., *Natural History of North American Amphibians and Reptiles*. D. Van Nostrand, 1955.

Pesson, Paul, *The World of Insects*. McGraw-Hill, 1959.

Peterson, Roger Tory, *A Field Guide to the Birds*. Houghton Mifflin, 1947.

Wallace, George J., *An Introduction to Ornithology*. Macmillan, 1963.

Forestry

Allen, Shirley W., and Grant William Sharpe, *An Introduction to American Forestry*. McGraw-Hill, 1960.

Carhart, Arthur H., *The National Forests*. Alfred A. Knopf, 1959.

Dana, Samuel, *Forest and Range Policy*. McGraw-Hill, 1956.

Lillard, Richard G., *The Great Forest*. Alfred A. Knopf, 1947.

Pinchot, Gifford, *Breaking New Ground*. Harcourt, Brace & World, 1947.

Thomas, William L., ed., *Man's Role in Changing the Face of the Earth*. University of Chicago Press, 1956.

U.S. Department of Agriculture, *Timber Resources for America's Future*. Government Printing Office, 1958.

Soil

* Farb, Peter, *Living Earth*. Harper & Row, 1959.

Lutz, Harold J., and Robert Chandler Jr., *Forest Soils*. John Wiley & Sons, 1946.

Russell, E. John, *The World of the Soil*. Collins, London, 1957.

Waksman, Selman A., *Soil Microbiology*. John Wiley & Sons, 1952.

Tree Guides

Benson, Lyman D., and R. A. Darrow, *A Manual of Southwestern Desert Trees and Shrubs*. University of Arizona Press, 1945.

† Harlow, William M., *Trees of the Eastern and Central United States and Canada*. Dover, 1957.

Harrar, Ellwood S., and J. G., *Guide to Southern Trees*. McGraw-Hill, 1946.

McMinn, Howard E., and Evelyn Maino, *An Illustrated Manual of Pacific Coast Trees*. University of California Press, 1946.

Peattie, Donald C., *A Natural History of Trees of Eastern and Central North America*. Houghton Mifflin, 1950.

Peattie, Donald C., *A Natural History of Western Trees*. Houghton Mifflin, 1953.

* Sargent, Charles S., *Manual of the Trees of North America* (2nd ed., 1922, 2 vols.). Dover, 1961.

General

Anderson, Edgar, *Plants, Man and Life*. Little, Brown, 1952.

Aubert de la Rüe, Edgar, François Bourlière and Jean-Paul Harroy. *The Tropics*. Alfred A. Knopf, 1957.

* Bates, Marston, *Where Winter Never Comes*. Charles Scribner's Sons, 1952.

* Bates, Marston, *The Forest and the Sea*. Random House, 1960.

* Christensen, Clyde M., *The Molds and Man*. University of Minnesota Press, 1961.

* Collis, John Stewart, *The Triumph of the Tree*. Sloane, 1954.

Haden-Guest, Stephen, and others, *World Geography of Forest Resources*. Ronald Press, 1956.

Lemmon, Robert Stell, and Charles C. Johnson, *Wildflowers of North America*. Hanover House, 1961.

McCormick, Jack, *The Living Forest*. Harper & Row, 1959.

Milne, Lorus J., and Margery J., *Biotic World and Man* (3rd ed.). Prentice-Hall, 1964.

Moldenke, Harold N., *American Wildflowers*. D. Van Nostrand, 1949.

Platt, Rutherford, *This Green World*. Dodd, Mead, 1952.

Simpson, George Gaylord, Colin S. Pittendrigh and Lewis S. Tiffany, *Life*. Harcourt, Brace & World, 1965.

Smith, Alexander H., *The Mushroom Hunter's Field Guide* (rev. ed.). University of Michigan Press, 1963.

* Storer, John H., *The Web of Life*. Devin, 1956; New American Library, 1956.

Teale, Edwin Way, *Autumn Across America*. Dodd, Mead, 1956.

U.S. Department of Agriculture, *Trees*. Government Printing Office, 1949.

Van Dersal, William R., *The American Land, Its History and Its Uses*. Oxford University Press, 1943.

* Also available in paperback edition

† Only available in paperback edition

Appendix

For the record, bigness in trees is arrived at by adding the circumference in inches, the total height in feet, and one quarter of the crown spread in feet. Thus a very tall, very slender tree may not be the biggest of its species; the total growth remains the criterion. These champions were chosen from a list compiled by The American Forestry Association. The list is updated as larger champions are discovered and reported by observers all over the country. Anyone discovering a record tree may write to: The American Forestry Association, 919 17th Street, N.W., Washington, D.C. 20006.

SPECIES	CIRCUMFERENCE AT 4½ FEET	HEIGHT	SPREAD	LOCATION
ALDER, Red or Oregon	13'-6"	76'	79'	Olympic Peninsula, Washington
ASH, Green	14'-7"	105'	79'	Big Oak Tree State Park, Missouri
White	22'-3"	80'	82'	Glen Mills, Pennsylvania
ASPEN, Bigtooth	17'-2"	95'	82'	Walker, New York
BALD CYPRESS, Common	39'-8"	122'-6"	47'	Weakley County, Tennessee
BEECH, American	15'-2"	106'	106'	Cumberstone, Maryland
BIRCH, Paper	10'-11"	96'	93'	Williamsburg, Michigan
BUCKEYE, Ohio	9'-6"	68'	64'	Highway 56, Webster County, Kentucky
CHERRY, Black	23'-4"	102'	89'	Lawrence, Michigan
CHESTNUT, American	15'-7 1/2"	90'	64'	Oregon City, Oregon
CYPRESS, Arizona	17'-5"	102'	38'	Coronado National Forest, Arizona
DOGWOOD, Flowering	5'-4"	30'	42'	Near Oriole, Maryland
DOUGLAS FIR, Common	53'-4"	221'	61'	Olympic National Park, Washington
ELM, American or White	24'-7"	160'	147'	Near Trigonia, Tennessee
FIR, Cascades or Pacific Silver	21'-5"	186'	38'	Olympic National Park, Washington
Noble	28'-4"	277'-11"	47'	Gifford Pinchot National Forest, Washington
Red or California Red	26'-3"	177'	--	Calaveras County, California
White	27'-8"	179'	34'	Mount Diablo Base, Meridian, California
HEMLOCK, Canada or Eastern	19'-9"	98'	69'	Great Smoky Mountains National Park, Tennessee
HICKORY, Shellbark	12'-3"	115'	90'	French Lick, Indiana
HOLLY, American	13'-4"	53'	61'	Near Hardin, Texas
HONEY LOCUST, Common	18'-9"	92'	112'	Near Queenstown, Maryland
LARCH, Eastern or Tamarack	11'-5"	60'	60'	Chaplin, Connecticut
LINDEN: BASSWOOD, American	17'-1"	103'	103'	Queenstown, Maryland
LOCUST, Black	15'-11"	85'	60'	Near Jefferson, Indiana
MAPLE, Red	16'-3"	125'	108'	Armada, Macomb County, Michigan
Silver	22'-10"	110'	93'	Felicity, Ohio
Sugar	19'-9"	116'	75'	Garrett County, Maryland
OAK, Black	22'-3"	125'	85'	Warrensville Heights, Ohio
Bur or Mossy Cup	20'-9"	110'	107'	Algonac, Michigan
Live	35'	78'	168'	Near Hahnville, Louisiana
Pin	16'	135'	135'	Saint Davids, Pennsylvania
PECAN	19'-7"	160'	95'	Near Mer Rouge, Louisiana
PINE, Jeffrey	23'-7"	175'	87'	Stanislaus National Forest, California
Loblolly	14'-1"	155'	72'	Near Urania, Louisiana
Ponderosa	21'-6"	223'	66'	Sierra National Forest, California
Shortleaf	10'-7"	146'	60'	Morganton, North Carolina
Sugar	32'-8"	220'	61'	Stanislaus National Forest, California
Western White	21'-3"	219'	36'	Near Elk River, Idaho
PLANE TREE: SYCAMORE, American	32'-10"	80'	102'	Near South Bloomfield, Ohio
POPLAR: COTTONWOOD, Eastern	25'-9"	131'	129'	Wayne, Michigan
RED CEDAR, Eastern	13'-4"	62'	42'	Cumberstone, Maryland
REDWOOD, Coast	65'-9"	361'	--	On Redwood Highway, California
SASSAFRAS, Common	16'	88'-6"	68'	Owensboro, Kentucky
SEQUOIA, Giant	101'-6" (at base)	272'	90'	Sequoia National Park, California
SPRUCE, Colorado or Blue	15'-8"	126'	36'	Gunnison National Forest, California
Engelmann	22'	179'	35'	Olympic National Park, Washington
Sitka	41'-8"	214'	50'	Olympic National Park, Washington
TULIP TREE: YELLOW POPLAR	26'-6"	83'	98'	Annapolis, Maryland
TUPELO, Black or Blackgum	16'-1"	130'	65'	Noxubee National Wildlife Refuge, Mississippi
WALNUT, Eastern Black	20'-3"	108'	128'	Anne Arundel County, Maryland
WILLOW, Black	26'-1"	85'	79'	Traverse City, Michigan

A Key to the Recognition of American Trees

This key to the trees of the United States was especially prepared for "The Forest" by Elbert L. Little Jr., Dendrologist of the U.S. Forest Service. It will enable you to identify all of the groups (genera) of native American and Canadian trees except for the tropical species of Hawaii and the southernmost parts of Florida, Texas and Arizona.

In using this key you will always be confronted by two choices. You must accept one and reject the other. To start, read through both statements numbered "1" at the beginning of the key. Only one of these two statements will apply to the tree you want to identify. At the end of the correct statement there will be either a number or a letter, telling you where to go next.

If there is a number, such as 2, proceed to the next statements numbered "2". Again there will be a pair of choices, but again only one will apply to your tree. Pick the right one and move on to the next number or letter that appears at the end of your choice.

Whenever in your eliminations you come to a letter, proceed to the section of the key with that letter: Part A, Part B, etc. Once you reach these sections, proceed as before by reading through both statements numbered "1" at the beginning of the sections and picking the appropriate one. At some point you will end up with a correct statement that is followed by the name of a tree. If you have made accurate choices this will be your tree.

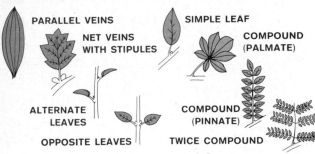

1. Leaves needlelike or scalelike, mostly evergreen, seeds usually borne exposed on scales of cone—conifers or softwoods . . . . Part A
1. Leaves broader (sometimes scalelike or absent on spiny trees), seeds not in a cone—flowering plants 2
   2. Leaves parallel-veined, evergreen, clustered at top of trunk or on few very stout branches—monocotyledons Part B
   2. Leaves net-veined (sometimes scalelike or absent on spiny trees)—dicotyledons (broadleaf trees or hardwoods) 3
3. Trees spiny, branches or twigs bearing spines or ending in spines, or leaves spiny-toothed and evergreen . . . . . . Part C
3. Trees without spines on branches, twigs or leaves 4
   4. Leaves evergreen . . . . Part D
   4. Leaves shedding in autumn (deciduous) 5
5. Leaves and usually twigs in pairs (opposite) or sometimes in threes . . . . Part E
5. Leaves and twigs single (alternate) 6
   6. Leaves not divided into leaflets (simple) . . . . Part F
   6. Leaves divided into leaflets (compound) . . . . Part G

PART A. CONIFERS OR SOFTWOODS

1. Leaves shedding in autumn (deciduous) 2
1. Leaves evergreen, both old and new present in summer . . 3
   2. Leaves in 2 rows on very slender twigs which also fall from tree—BALD CYPRESS (*Taxodium distichum*)
   2. Leaves many in cluster on short spurs—LARCH, TAMARACK (*Larix*)
3. Leaves needlelike, more than ½ inch long 4
3. Leaves scalelike, overlapping, less than ¼ inch long, or partly needlelike to ¾ inch long 10
   4. Needles in clusters of 2 to 5 (rarely 1), with sheath at base—PINE (*Pinus*)
   4. Needles borne singly, without sheath at base 5
5. Twigs rough with peglike bases of old needles 6
5. Twigs smooth or nearly so 9
   6. Needles soft, blunt-pointed—HEMLOCK (*Tsuga*)
   6. Needles stiff, sharp-pointed 7
7. Needles spreading around twig, mostly 4-angled—SPRUCE (*Picea*)
7. Needles in 2 rows, flattened 8
   8. Needles short-pointed, shorter than 1 inch—YEW (*Taxus*)
   8. Needles long-pointed, longer than 1 inch—TORREYA (*Torreya*)
9. Leafstalks short, cones hanging down—DOUGLAS FIR (*Pseudotsuga*)
9. Leafstalks none, cones upright in top of tree—FIR (*Abies*)
   10. Leaves single—SEQUOIA, REDWOOD (*Sequoia*)
   10. Leaves in pairs, threes or fours 11
11. Leafy twigs more or less flattened 12
11. Leafy twigs rounded or 4-angled 14
   12. Leafy twigs slightly flattened, less than 1/16 inch across leaves—WHITE CEDAR (*Chamaecyparis*)
   12. Leafy twigs much flattened, more than 1/16 inch across leaves 13
13. Joints of leafy twigs longer than broad—INCENSE CEDAR (*Libocedrus decurrens*)
13. Joints of leafy twigs about as long as broad—THUJA (*Thuja*)
   14. Leafy twigs regularly branched almost at right angles; seeds in hard cone—CYPRESS (*Cupressus*)
   14. Leafy twigs irregularly branched at sharp angles; seeds in "berry"—JUNIPER (*Juniperus*)

PART B. MONOCOTYLEDONS

1. Leaves without leafstalk, narrow, grasslike or bayonetlike—YUCCA (*Yucca*)
1. Leaves with long leafstalk, very large, fan-shaped—CABBAGE PALMETTO (*Sabal palmetto*) and other PALMS (*palm family*)

PART C. SPINY TREES

1. Branches swollen, green, soft and watery, with many clusters of sharp, spreading spines (cactus family) 2
1. Branches not swollen, hard; twigs or leaves spiny 3
   2. Branches jointed, round or flattened—CHOLLA, PRICKLY PEAR (*Opuntia*)
   2. Branches not jointed, round, with long ridges and grooves—CEREUS (*Cereus*)
3. Leaves absent, scalelike, or small and usually shed 4

3. Leaves normal, present through growing season..... 10
    4. Twigs gray, with gland dots, ending in spines; leaves less than 1 inch long—SMOKETHORN (*Dalea spinosa*)
    4. Twigs and usually branches green 5
5. Spines formed by sharp ends of twigs........... 6
5. Spines along twigs at nodes, leaves twice compound.... 9
    6. Twigs with long whitish lines, flexible, upright, in broom-like masses—CANOTIA (*Canotia holacantha*)
    6. Twigs without long lines, stiff, spreading.......... 7
7. Twigs branching at small angles, gray-green—HOLACANTHA (*Holacantha emoryi*)
7. Twigs branching at wide angles.................. 8
    8. Twigs mostly dark green, leaves scalelike—ALLTHORN (*Koeberlinia spinosa*)
    8. Twigs and bark yellow-green, leaves twice compound—PALOVERDE (*Cercidium*)
9. Spines single at nodes—PALOVERDE (*Cercidium*)
9. Spines paired at nodes, a third, larger spine ending short leaf axis—JERUSALEM THORN (*Parkinsonia aculeata*)
    10. Leaves divided into leaflets (compound).......... 11
    10. Leaves not divided into leaflets (simple).......... 19
11. Leaves twice compound, more than 2 feet long, spines on leaf axes and twigs — DEVIL'S-WALKING-STICK (*Aralia spinosa*)
11. Leaves less than 1 foot long 12
    12. Leaflets of once compound leaves with strong odor when crushed; small spines at nodes, stout spines on trunk—PRICKLY ASH (*Zanthoxylum*)
    12. Leaflets and spines not as above; fruit a pod with bean-like seeds (legume family) 13
13. Spines partly branched, becoming 3 to 5 inches long; leaves once and twice compound—HONEY LOCUST (*Gleditsia*)
13. Spines not branched, less than 1 inch long.......... 14
    14. Spines scattered singly along twigs not at nodes, curved or hooked, less than ¼ inch long—ACACIA (*Acacia*)
    14. Spines usually paired at nodes, straight.......... 15
15. Leaves twice compound (bipinnate) 16
15. Leaves once compound (pinnate) 18
    16. Leaves with usually 2, sometimes 4, paired forks—MESQUITE (*Prosopis*)
    16. Leaves with 6 or more paired forks............ 17
17. Leaflets less than ¼ inch long—ACACIA (*Acacia*)
17. Leaflets more than ¼ inch long—LEAD TREE (*Leucaena*)
    18. Leaflets with minute bristle tip, leaves deciduous—LOCUST (*Robinia*)
    18. Leaflets without bristle tip, leaves evergreen or nearly so—TESOTA (*Olneya tesota*)
19. Leaves not spiny or evergreen.................. 20
19. Leaves spiny-toothed, evergreen................ 27
    20. Spines formed by sharp ends of twigs.......... 21
    20. Spines at nodes or scattered along twigs......... 26
21. Leaves paired (opposite), covered with silvery scales—SILVER BUFFALO BERRY (*Shepherdia argentea*)
21. Leaves not paired or covered with silvery scales...... 22
    22. Leaves often clustered and crowded, narrowly elliptic, edges not toothed—BUMELIA (*Bumelia*)
    22. Leaves borne singly (alternate)............. 23
23. Leaves rounded at apex, veins inconspicuous........ 24
23. Leaves pointed at apex, veins conspicuous.......... 25
    24. Leaves less than ¾ inch long, not toothed—CONDALIA (*Condalia*)
    24. Leaves 1 to 1½ inches long, sometimes toothed—SPINY CEANOTHUS (*Ceanothus spinosus*)
25. Leaves finely, evenly saw-toothed — PLUM, CHERRY (*Prunus*)

25. Leaves coarsely toothed, often lobed—CRAB APPLE (*Malus*)
    26. Leaves finely toothed, often lobed; spines slender, sharp, reddish brown—HAWTHORN (*Crataegus*)
    26. Leaves not toothed; spines stout, gray, single at nodes; juice milky—OSAGE ORANGE (*Maclura pomifera*)
27. Winter buds 3 or more clustered at tip of twig; fruit an acorn—OAK (*Quercus*)
27. Winter buds 1 or absent at tip of twig; fruit not an acorn 28
    28. Leaves wavy with few large spiny teeth—AMERICAN HOLLY (*Ilex opaca*)
    28. Leaves with many small, even, spiny teeth........ 29
29. Leaves rounded, less than 1½ inches long, twigs often ending in spines—HOLLYLEAF BUCKTHORN (*Rhamnus crocea*)
29. Leaves elliptic or narrower, mostly more than 1½ inches long; twigs not ending in spines 30
    30. Twigs bright reddish brown—LEMONADE SUMAC (*Rhus integrifolia*)
    30. Twigs yellow or orange when young — HOLLYLEAF CHERRY (*Prunus ilicifolia*)

PART D. BROADLEAF SPINELESS EVERGREENS

1. Leaves and usually twigs in pairs (opposite)......... 2
1. Leaves single (alternate) or crowded.............. 5
    2. Leaves simple and toothed or divided into leaflets (compound) 3
    2. Leaves simple, not toothed.................... 4
3. Leaves simple and toothed or divided into 3 to 8 narrow, lobed leaflets—LYONTREE (*Lyonothamnus floribundus*)
3. Leaves divided into 8 to 16 narrow, paired leaflets—TEXAS PORLIERIA (*Porlieria angustifolia*)
    4. Twigs with rings at nodes, 4-angled when young—WAVY-LEAF SILK-TASSEL (*Garrya elliptica*)
    4. Twigs without rings at nodes, round—OSMANTHUS (*Osmanthus*)
5. Leaves divided into leaflets (compound, pinnate) 6
5. Leaves simple 7
    6. Leaflets slightly curved to one side or sickle-shaped—TEXAS PISTACHE (*Pistacia texana*)
    6. Leaflets elliptic—MESCALBEAN (*Sophora secundiflora*)
7. Leaves ¼ to ½ inch long, wedge-shaped, with 3 to 7 very narrow lobes, crowded—CLIFF ROSE (*Cowania stansburiana*)
7. Leaves more than ½ inch long 8
    8. Leaves with 3 main veins from base 9
    8. Leaves with 1 main vein.................... 10
9. Leaves 3-lobed with rounded lobes, ½ to 1½ inches long and broad—FREMONTIA (*Fremontia*)
9. Leaves elliptic, edges toothed—CEANOTHUS (*Ceanothus*)
    10. Winter buds 3 or more clustered at tip of twig; fruit an acorn 11
    10. Winter buds 1 or none at tip of twig; fruit not an acorn 12
11. Leaves with many parallel veins and usually many small, wavy teeth; scales of acorn cup more than ⅛ inch long—TAN OAK (*Lithocarpus densiflorus*)
11. Leaves not as above; scales of acorn cup small and inconspicuous—OAK (*Quercus*)
    12. Leaf edges toothed......................... 13
    12. Leaf edges not toothed..................... 23
13. Leaves without scales (stipules) at base............ 14
13. Leaves with scales (stipules) at base.............. 17
    14. Leaves with minute gland dots, aromatic BAYBERRY (*Myrica*)
    14. Leaves not gland-dotted or aromatic............ 15

15. Leaves 1½ to 3 inches long, sometimes without teeth—LEMONADE SUMAC (*Rhus integrifolia*)

15. Leaves more than 4 inches long 16

16. Leaves dark green, shiny, hairless—LOBLOLLY BAY (*Gordonia lasianthus*)

16. Leaves yellow-green, slightly hairy beneath, with sweetish taste—COMMON SWEETLEAF (*Symplocos tinctoria*)

17. Lateral veins extending to teeth—CERCOCARPUS (*Cercocarpus*)

17. Lateral veins curved and joined within border 18

18. Twigs hairy; leaves lance-shaped, teeth not spiny . . . 19

18. Twigs not hairy; leaves broader, teeth mostly spiny 20

19. Leaves yellow-green, hairy beneath—TORREY VAUQUELINIA (*Vauquelinia californica*)

19. Leaves shiny, dark green, hairless—CHRISTMASBERRY (*Photinia arbutifolia*)

20. Leaves wavy with few large spiny teeth—AMERICAN HOLLY (*Ilex opaca*)

20. Leaves with many small teeth 21

21. Leaves with small wavy teeth—YAUPON (*Ilex vomitoria*)

21. Leaves with many small spiny teeth 22

22. Leaves rounded, less than 1½ inches long—HOLLYLEAF BUCKTHORN (*Rhamnus crocea*)

22. Leaves elliptic or narrower, mostly more than 1½ inches long—HOLLYLEAF CHERRY (*Prunus ilicifolia*)

23. Leaves with scales (stipules) at base 24

23. Leaves with no scales (stipules) at base 28

24. Twigs with rings at nodes—MAGNOLIA (*Magnolia*)

24. Twigs without rings 25

25. Leaves mostly crowded at end of twigs—CERCOCARPUS (*Cercocarpus*)

25. Leaves not crowded 26

26. Leaves with coat of golden-yellow scales beneath—GOLDEN CHINKAPIN (*Castanopsis chrysophylla*)

26. Leaves green beneath 27

27. Leaves with odor and bitter taste of cherry—CHERRY (*Prunus*)

27. Leaves without distinctive odor or taste—HOLLY (*Ilex*)

28. Leaves aromatic when crushed 29

28. Leaves not aromatic when crushed 32

29. Leaves with minute gland dots—BAYBERRY (*Myrica*)

29. Leaves not gland-dotted 30

30. Twigs green, leaves with prominent network of small veins beneath—CALIFORNIA LAUREL (*Umbellularia californica*)

30. Twigs brownish, leaves with small veins not prominent 31

31. Leaves with small veins inconspicuous beneath, with pleasant odor—PERSEA (*Persea*)

31. Leaves without visible small veins, with unpleasant odor—ANISE TREE (*Illicium*)

32. Leaves sharp-pointed at apex 33

32. Leaves rounded or blunt-pointed at apex 37

33. Leaves rough, hairy above—ANAQUA (*Ehretia anacua*)

33. Leaves smooth above 34

34. Leaves covered beneath with rusty or pale scales—TREE LYONIA (*Lyonia ferruginea*)

34. Leaves hairless or nearly so beneath 35

35. Leaves large, 4 to 12 inches long—RHODODENDRON (*Rhododendron*)

35. Leaves less than 5 inches long 36

36. Twigs greenish, leaves with veins obscure beneath—MOUNTAIN LAUREL (*Kalmia latifolia*)

36. Twigs reddish, leaves with prominent veins beneath—MADRONE (*Arbutus*)

37. Leaves elliptic to oblong, rounded at base—SUMAC (*Rhus*)

37. Leaves wedge-shaped at base 38

38. Leaves obscurely veined beneath—BUCKWHEAT TREE (*Cliftonia monophylla*)

38. Leaves with prominent network of small veins beneath 39

39. Leaves narrowly oblong—CYRILLA (*Cyrilla*)

39. Leaves elliptic to nearly round—TREE SPARKLEBERRY (*Vaccinium arboreum*)

PART E. TREES WITH OPPOSITE LEAVES

1. Leaves or leaflets very narrow 2

1. Leaves broad 3

2. Leaves simple, partly single (alternate)—DESERT WILLOW (*Chilopsis linearis*)

2. Leaves divided into 8 to 16 paired leaflets, evergreen—TEXAS PORLIERIA (*Porlieria angustifolia*)

3. Leaves in threes or partly in pairs (opposite) 4

3. Leaves uniformly in pairs (opposite) 5

4. Leaves heart-shaped, broadest near base — CATALPA (*Catalpa*)

4. Leaves elliptic, broadest near middle — BUTTONBUSH (*Cephalanthus occidentalis*)

5. Leaves thick, leathery, evergreen 6

5. Leaves thin, shedding in autumn 8

6. Leaves simple and toothed or divided into 3 to 8 narrow, deeply lobed leaflets—LYONTREE (*Lyonothamnus floribundus*)

6. Leaves simple, edges not toothed 7

7. Twigs with rings at nodes, 4-angled when young—WAVYLEAF SILK-TASSEL (*Garrya elliptica*)

7. Twigs without rings, round—OSMANTHUS (*Osmanthus*)

8. Leaves divided into leaflets (compound) 9

8. Leaves not divided into leaflets (simple) 13

9. Leaflets 5 or 7, spreading fingerlike from end of leafstalk (palmate)—BUCKEYE (*Aesculus*)

9. Leaflets 3 to 9, attached along extended leafstalk (pinnate) 10

10. Leaflets bluntly or not toothed, with veins curved within edges—ASH (*Fraxinus*)

10. Leaflets sharply toothed, veins extending to teeth . . 11

11. Twigs stout with thick pith, leaflets 5 to 9—ELDER (*Sambucus*)

12. Leaflets 3, finely saw-toothed—BLADDERNUT (*Staphylea*)

12. Leaflets 3, sometimes 5 or 7, coarsely toothed with few large teeth—BOX ELDER (*Acer negundo*)

13. Leaf edges toothed 14

13. Leaf edges not toothed 17

14. Leaves deeply 3- or 5-lobed—MAPLE (*Acer*)

14. Leaves not lobed 15

15. Twigs 4-angled—EUONYMUS (*Euonymus*)

15. Twigs round 16

16. Winter buds with 2 paired scales—VIBURNUM (*Viburnum*)

16. Winter buds with several scales—FORESTIERA (*Forestiera*)

17. Leaves covered with silvery scales, twigs ending in spines—SILVER BUFFALO BERRY (*Shepherdia argentea*)

17. Leaves not covered with scales, twigs not spiny 18

18. Leaves with paired scales (stipules) remaining at base—PINCKNEYA (*Pinckneya pubens*)

18. Leaves without scales (stipules) at base 19

19. Lateral veins long, curved, twigs with rings at nodes—DOGWOOD (*Cornus*)

19. Lateral veins mostly straight, twigs without rings 20
   20. Twigs 4-angled, leaves less than 2 inches long or with 3 or 5 leaflets—SINGLE-LEAF ASH (*Fraxinus anomala*)
   20. Twigs round or nearly so; leaves more than 4 inches long —FRINGE TREE (*Chionanthus virginicus*)

PART F. TREES WITH ALTERNATE, SIMPLE, DECIDUOUS LEAVES AND WITHOUT SPINES

1. Winter buds 3 or more clustered at tip of twig; fruit an acorn—OAK (*Quercus*)
1. Winter buds 1 or none at tip of twig; fruit not an acorn . . 2
   2. Winter buds covered by 1 scale; leaves usually narrow, usually finely toothed, leafstalk short—WILLOW (*Salix*)
   2. Winter buds with more than 1 scale or none; leaves various 3
3. Twigs bright green, leaves not toothed but often with 2 or 3 rounded lobes, spicy—SASSAFRAS (*Sassafras albidum*)
3. Twigs brown or gray except when young, leaves various 4
   4. Leaf edges neither toothed nor lobed 5
   4. Leaf edges toothed or lobed or both 16
5. Twigs with rings at nodes—MAGNOLIA (*Magnolia*)
5. Twigs without rings 6
   6. Leaves 8 to 12 inches long—PAWPAW (*Asimina triloba*)
   6. Leaves smaller 7
7. Leaves very long and narrow, less than ⅜ inch broad— DESERT WILLOW (*Chilopsis.linearis*)
7. Leaves broad 8
   8. Leaves with 3 or more main veins from base 9
   8. Leaves with 1 main vein 10
9. Leaves with 5 or 7 main veins from base—REDBUD (*Cercis*)
9. Leaves with 3 main veins from base—HACKBERRY (*Celtis*)
   10. Leafstalks more than 1 inch long 11
   10. Leafstalks less than 1 inch long 12
11. Leaves elliptic with long curved lateral veins—ALTERNATE LEAF DOGWOOD (*Cornus alternifolia*)
11. Leaves broadly lance-shaped with short lateral veins— CORKWOOD (*Leitneria floridana*)
   12. Twigs with terminal bud 13
   12. Twigs without terminal bud 15
13. Leafstalks abruptly enlarged at base—ELLIOTTIA (*Elliottia racemosa*)
13. Leafstalks not enlarged at base 14
   14. Leaves short-pointed at apex—TUPELO (*Nyssa*)
   14. Leaves rounded at apex—AMERICAN SMOKE TREE (*Cotinus obovatus*)
15. Leaves with star-shaped hairs beneath—BIGLEAF SNOWBELL (*Styrax grandifolia*)
15. Leaves with unbranched hairs or none — PERSIMMON (*Diospyros*)
   16. Leaves with 3 to 7 spreading lobes 17
   16. Leaves not lobed or with lobes along both sides from main vein 19
17. Leaves with broad, nearly straight, slightly notched apex and 4 or 6 shallow lobes, not toothed—YELLOW POPLAR (*Liriodendron tulipifera*)
17. Leaves with pointed apex and odd number of toothed lobes 18
   18. Lateral buds visible at base of leafstalk—SWEET GUM (*Liquidambar styraciflua*)
   18. Lateral buds covered by base of leafstalk—SYCAMORE (*Platanus*)
19. Leaves with the 2 sides unequal at base 20
19. Leaves with both sides equal 24
   20. Leaves with few wavy teeth beyond middle—WITCH

HAZEL (*Hamamelis virginiana*)
   20. Leaves with sharp-pointed teeth 21
21. Leafstalks more than 1 inch long, leaves nearly as broad as long, heart-shaped—BASSWOOD (*Tilia*)
21. Leafstalks less than ½ inch long, leaves much longer than broad 22
   22. Leaves with 3 main veins from base—HACKBERRY (*Celtis*)
   22. Leaves with 1 main vein 23
23. Leaves with uneven teeth of 2 sizes alternating—ELM (*Ulmus*)
23. Leaves with even, uniform teeth—PLANER TREE (*Planera aquatica*)
   24. Leaves wedge-shaped with few teeth; shrubs, rarely small trees 25
   24. Leaves broader, with many teeth 26
25. Leaves with silver hairs and usually 3 teeth at apex, aromatic—BIG SAGEBRUSH (*Artemisia tridentata*)
25. Leaves light green, hairless, with few teeth on sides, not aromatic—EASTERN BACCHARIS (*Baccharis halimifolia*)
   26. Leafstalks nearly as long as blade, often flattened—COTTONWOOD, POPLAR, ASPEN (*Populus*)
   26. Leafstalks less than half as long as blade, round 27
27. Leaves with uneven teeth of 2 sizes 28
27. Leaves with even, uniformed teeth or both toothed and lobed 32
   28. Winter buds stalked, covered usually by 3 scales not overlapping—ALDER (*Alnus*)
   28. Winter buds not stalked, with overlapping scales . . . 29
29. Leaves nearly round, tip rounded or short-pointed—HAZEL (*Corylus*)
29. Leaves narrower, tip long- or short-pointed 30
   30. Leaves blue-green—AMERICAN HORNBEAM (*Carpinus caroliniana*)
   30. Leaves yellow-green 31
31. Leafstalks less than ¼ inch long — HOP HORNBEAM (*Ostrya*)
31. Leafstalks ¼ to 1 inch long—BIRCH (*Betula*)
   32. Leaves with many straight, closely parallel lateral veins, coarsely toothed 33
   32. Leaves with lateral veins curved or not closely parallel, variously toothed or also lobed 34
33. Leaves about twice as long as wide—AMERICAN BEECH (*Fagus grandifolia*)
33. Leaves 3 or more times as long as wide—CHESTNUT, CHINKAPIN (*Castanea*)
   34. Leaves with scales (stipules) at base, often shedding 35
   34. Leaves without scales (stipules) at base 39
35. Winter buds naked, leaves inconspicuously wavy-toothed —BUCKHORN (*Rhamnus*)
35. Winter buds with overlapping scales, leaves with sharp teeth 36
   36. Winter buds long and narrow—SERVICEBERRY (*Amelanchier*)
   36. Winter buds not elongated, twigs often spiny 37
37. Leaves finely, evenly saw-toothed, often with odor and bitter taste of cherry—PLUM, CHERRY (*Prunus*)
37. Leaves often lobed, without odor and taste of cherry 38
   38. Leaves finely toothed, lobed or long-tapering at base, folded together lengthwise in bud—HAWTHORN (*Crataegus*)
   38. Leaves coarsely toothed, often lobed, rolled inward in bud—APPLE, CRAB APPLE (*Malus*)
39. Leaves hairless or nearly so, shiny green, with sour taste —SOURWOOD (*Oxydendrum arboreum*)

39. Leaves hairy beneath 40
   40. Leaves with star-shaped hairs—SILVER BELL (*Halesia*)
   40. Leaves with straight hairs 41
41. Leaves with small wavy teeth, with sweetish taste—COMMON SWEETLEAF (*Symplocos tinctoria*)
41. Leaves with small sharp teeth 42
   42. Leaves finely saw-toothed—CINNAMON CLETHRA (*Clethra acuminata*)
   42. Leaves with minute distant teeth ⅛ to ⅜ inch apart—STEWARTIA (*Stewartia*)

PART G. TREES WITH ALTERNATE, COMPOUND, DECIDUOUS LEAVES AND WITHOUT SPINES

1. Leaflets 3, long-pointed at both ends—HOP TREE (*Ptelea*)
1. Leaflets 5 or more, attached along extended leafstalk . . . 2
   2. Leaves twice compound (bipinnate)—KENTUCKY COFFEE TREE (*Gymnocladus dioicus*)
   2. Leaves once compound (pinnate) 3
3. Twigs with colored sticky juice 4
3. Twigs with watery juice 5
   4. Juice turning black on exposure—POISON SUMAC (*Toxicodendron vernix*)

   4. Juice whitish, not poisonous—SUMAC (*Rhus*)
5. Leaflets not toothed 6
5. Leaflets toothed 9
   6. Leaflets slightly curved to one side or sickle-shaped—SOAPBERRY (*Sapindus*)
   6. Leaflets with sides equal 7
7. Leaflets more than 2 inches long—YELLOWWOOD (*Cladrastis lutea*)
7. Leaflets less than 1½ inches long 8
   8. Leaflets 21 to 45, with brown gland dots beneath, resinous—KIDNEYWOOD (*Eysenhardtia polystachya*)
   8. Leaflets 9 to 19, without gland dots, not resinous—TEXAS SOPHORA (*Sophora affinis*)
9. Twigs with rings at nodes—MOUNTAIN ASH (*Sorbus*)
9. Twigs without rings 10
   10. Leaflets not aromatic, winter buds about ⅛ inch long—MEXICAN BUCKEYE (*Ungnadia speciosa*)
   10. Leaflets aromatic when crushed, winter buds larger 11
11. Leaflets 11 to 23, winter buds naked, pith of twigs in plates—WALNUT (*Juglans*)
11. Leaflets 5 to 17, winter buds covered with scales, pith of twigs solid—HICKORY, PECAN (*Carya*)

Picture Credits *Credits for pictures from left to right are separated by commas, top to bottom by dashes.*

Cover: Brett Weston from Rapho-Guillumette. 8: N.R. Farbman. 10, 15: Drawings by Kenneth Gosner. 17: Jack Dermid. 18: Jack Dermid, W. H. Hodge. 19: Richard Meek for SPORTS ILLUSTRATED. 20, 21: Jack Dermid—Wallace Kirkland, Dr. C. G. Hampson. 22, 23: Hugh Morton from Alpha Photo Associates, Inc., Jack Dermid. 24, 25: Dr. Miles Pirnie—John H. Gerard, Jack Dermid. 26, 27 Helen Cruickshank from National Audubon Society. 28, 29: Dr. Carnes Weeks, Alicia Hills, Leonard Lee Rue III from Monkmeyer Press Photos—Jack Dermid. 30, 31: Rudolf Freund. 32: Louis Quitt from Monkmeyer Press Photos. 33: Roy Pinney from National Audubon Society. 34, 35: Ansel Adams from Magnum, Jack Dermid—Don Wooldridge. 36, 37: Andreas Feininger. 38: Dr. Henry N. Andrews. 40 through 45: Kenneth Gosner. 47: Josef Muench from *Historical Geology* by Carl O. Dunbar courtesy John Wiley & Sons Inc. 48: Kenneth Gosner. 49 through 55: *Prehistoric Animals* published by Paul Hamlyn. 56: A. Y. Owen. 60, 61: Kenneth Gosner. 62, 63: Matt Greene; based on Goode's Homolosine Equal-Area Projection, Copyright by the University of Chicago Press. 64: J. R. Eyerman. 65: Leo M. Oestreicher—Fritz Goro—U.S. Forest Service. 66, 67: J. R. Eyerman. 68, 69: Jerry Cooke—Peter Stackpole, Eliot Elisofon. 70, 71: left E. Aubert de la Rüe; center Josef Muench—W. H. Hodge; right W. H. Hodge. 72: E. Aubert de la Rüe. 74: Kenneth Gosner. 81: Chuck Abbott from Rapho-Guillumette. 82 through 91: Steven C. Wilson. 92: Dr. Roman Vishniac. 96, 97: Kenneth Gosner. 101: William Harlow. 102 through 105: Jack J. Kunz. 106: all William Harlow except top right Leonard Lee Rue III from Monkmeyer Press Photos; bottom center Rutherford Platt.

107: Rutherford Platt. 108, 109: W. H. Hodge—Alfred Eisenstaedt, E. Aubert de la Rüe, Ross E. Hutchins—W. H. Hodge—E. Aubert de la Rüe. 110: E. Aubert de la Rüe, *Parcs Nationaux du Congo*, W. H. Hodge, E. Aubert de la Rüe—E. Aubert de la Rüe, W. H. Hodge. 111: all E. Aubert de la Rüe except bottom left Hamilton Wright. 112: Ylla from Rapho-Guillumette. 116, 117: Kenneth Gosner. 119: Louis Renault from Photo Researchers, Inc. 120, 121: Dorien Leigh from Black Star, A.B.C. from Black Star. 122: Louis Renault from Photo Researchers, Inc.—P. J. Corson from Rapho-Guillumette. 123: Colin Turnbull. 124, 125: Bassett Maguire, Fulvio Roiter. 126, 127: Bassett Maguire. 128: George B. Schaller. 129: Barbara Harrisson. 130: Leonard Lee Rue III from Monkmeyer Press Photos. 132 through 135: Kenneth Gosner. 137: Dr. Roman Vishniac. 138, 139: Steven C. Wilson, Dr. Roman Vishniac. 140, 141: A. B. Klots from Monkmeyer Press Photos (2), Ross E. Hutchins, Lee Jenkins from Monkmeyer Press Photos—E. S. Ross. 142, 143: Ross E. Hutchins. 144, 145: A. B. Klots. 146, 147: Rudolf Freund. 148: U.S. Public Health Service. 149: Courtesy Syntex Chemical Company. 150: U.S. Forest Service. 153: Kenneth Gosner. 159: U.S. Forest Service. 160, 161: U.S. Forest Service—Culver Pictures. 162, 163: Culver Pictures, U.S. Forest Service—American Forest Products Industries, Inc. 164: U.S. Forest Service—Culver Pictures—Dmitri Kessel. 165: Allan Grant. 166, 167: Ray Atkeson. 168: J. R. Eyerman. 175: American Forest Products Industries, Inc. 176, 177: Ralph Crane from Black Star. 179: N. R. Farbman. 180, 181: Gabriel Benzur—American Forest Products Industries, Inc.

Acknowledgments

The editors of this book are particularly indebted to these authorities: Bassett Maguire, New York Botanical Garden, who read and criticized the entire book; Marcia Brody, Watson Laboratories, IBM, and Jack McCormick, The Academy of Natural Sciences of Philadelphia, who provided valuable advice in their areas of study. The editors are also indebted to the following individuals: Stephen W. Blodgett, The Conservation Foundation; H. A. Borthwick, U.S. Department of Agriculture; William A. Burns, Witte Memorial Museum, San Antonio, Texas; Guyton DeLoach, Georgia Forest Research Council; Erling Dorf, Princeton University; Carl O. Dunbar and Percy A. Morris, Yale University; Alexander B. Klots, City College, New York; Hugh Raup, Harvard University; David J. Rogers, New York Botanical Garden; Alexander H. Smith, University of Michigan; Colin Turnbull, The American Museum of Natural History; Eugene H. Varney, Rutgers University; and to these organizations: American Forest Products Industries, Inc.; The American Forestry Association; the Weyerhaeuser Co.; and the U.S. Forest Service and its regional foresters.

Index

✕✕✕✕✕✕

PRODUCTION STAFF FOR TIME INCORPORATED
*John L. Hallenbeck (Vice President and Director of Production), Robert E. Foy and Caroline Ferri
Text photocomposed under the direction of Albert J. Dunn*